Engineering
and the
Liberal Arts

McGRAW-HILL SERIES
IN CONTINUING EDUCATION
FOR ENGINEERS

Florman ENGINEERING AND THE LIBERAL ARTS

Engineering
and the
Liberal Arts

A Technologist's Guide
to History, Literature, Philosophy,
Art, and Music

Samuel C. Florman, P.E.

Vice President and General Manager
Kreisler-Borg Construction Company, Inc.
Scarsdale, New York

McGRAW-HILL BOOK COMPANY

New York   San Francisco   Toronto   London   Sydney

ENGINEERING AND THE LIBERAL ARTS

For Judy

Preface

The purpose of this book is fourfold:

1. To advocate the cause of liberal education for engineers;

2. To explore some of the ways in which engineering is related to the liberal arts, thereby providing natural bridges of interest and concern between the "two cultures";

3. To give the average engineer a quick "refresher," by reviewing in broad outline the nature and content of the liberal arts;

4. To induce the engineer to journey deep into the world of the liberal arts and to recommend some of the likeliest paths for him to take.

In writing this book I offer as credentials, not academic authority—for my career is in engineering and construction—but life-long study and delight in the liberal arts, and many years of thinking and writing about their relationship to engineering.

The philosophy that underlies this book was shaped in large measure under the influence of teachers at the Fieldston School, Dartmouth College (including the Thayer School of Engineering), and Columbia University. At these three institutions there exists an exemplary respect both for technology and the humanities.

Portions of several chapters have appeared previously in *American Engineer, Civil Engineering,* and *Consulting Engineer.* I am grateful to the editors of these publications for their encouragement and for permission to reuse this material.

I thank my friends at Kreisler-Borg Construction Company for working a little harder on those days when I retired to my ivory tower to write. I thank my wife for researching, editing, and proofreading, and for her continuing encouragement.

Samuel C. Florman

Contents

CHAPTER ONE

The
Civilized
Engineer

Those of us who are engineers in the last third of the twentieth century are among the most fortunate of men.

In a time of widespread despair our constructive work gives us reason to be sanguine. In an age when most men are confused by the complexity of the scientific revolution, we are uniquely equipped to understand and enjoy the marvelous technological happenings all about us. It is said that the condition of man in our era is one of increasing alienation. But we engineers are needed by our fellow men; our place in society is secure; we feel at home in the world. Our work brings us comfortably in touch with the real world of "things"; our days are spiced with the tang of novelty and inventiveness. Financially, although we might not always consider ourselves adequately compensated for our efforts, we need never know want.

Busy, secure, and dissatisfied

Nevertheless, we are not content. We can see that the world is teeming with treasures of the arts about which we know little. We find ourselves somehow excluded from the intellectual and philosophical discourse in which the values and goals of our society are shaped. Not only are we not participating in the artistic and intellectual life of our time, but we find that our professional product, the technology of which we are so proud, is being misused and misdirected, dominated by forces beyond our control. We are unhappy about our "image" and about the fact that we are not receiving our proper share of respect and responsibility.

In sum, we may be busy and secure, but we are far from satisfied, either with our personal lives or with our role in society. Anyone familiar with the literature of our professional journals knows this to be the case.

Our dissatisfaction seems related to a certain flaw in our professional personality, a flaw which limits both our capacity to experience life to the full and our ability to play an important role in the political, cultural, and social developments of our time. This flaw stems from our failure to become "well rounded," a failure resulting from our admitted concentration on the technical aspect of our profession. To pinpoint it, the source of both our inadequacy and our discontent is rooted in our lack of a broadly based education, our lack of a civilizing education in the liberal arts.

According to Webster's dictionary, civilization consists of

"progress in education, refinement of taste and feeling, and the arts that constitute culture." If we take this definition literally, the average engineer today is simply not civilized. It is paradoxical that without us civilization could not exist, yet we are somehow isolated from the civilizing influence of the culture of our time. This is a misfortune for us as individuals, for our profession, and for the world.

I am not talking about superficial refinement and the ability to sparkle at cocktail parties. I am talking about something more fundamental. It is not an exaggeration to say that liberal education for engineers could improve the quality of life for the average engineer, contribute to the sound development of the engineering profession, and help to preserve and enrich society as a whole. Let us consider some of the ways in which this is so.

Intellectual competence and imagination

First of all, a liberal education enlarges intellectual capacity, develops mental agility, improves our ability to think. As a noted educator has said, liberal education helps "to cultivate those skills and habits of reasoning which constitute intellectual competence, the capacity to think logically and clearly, the ability to organize one's thoughts on any subject on which essential facts are possessed or obtainable."[1]

If we need the liberal arts to maintain and improve our intellectual competence, we need them even more to develop imagination, for without imagination reason is not equal to even the minimum demands of our exploding technology. Lewis Mumford has warned us that a concentration on pure technical training

> . . . might defeat even its immediate purposes by depriving original minds of the stimulus and enrichment of wider interests and activities.

Has not Niels Bohr told us that he arrived at the doctrine of complementarity in physics by speculating on an ancient theological dilemma—the impossibility of reconciling perfect love with perfect justice? Men flew in dreams and communicated instantaneously in myths and fairy stories long before they achieved the technical apparatus for doing so. But would any chain of discoveries and inventions have produced a balloon or a telegraph if the dream had not first suggested these goals? Many significant inventions, from the helicopter to the motion picture, began as toys for amusing the young. Plainly the self-sufficiency of the specialist's world is a prisoner's illusion. It is time to open the gates.[2]

Liberal education and leadership

As liberal education improves our intellectual competence and expands our imagination, it also develops those qualities of intellectual curiosity and general understanding, those traits of grace and wit and poise which characterize the leaders among men. Too often engineers are found lacking in these attributes. Scientifically made personality studies have revealed engineers to be "socially conforming, impersonal, introverted individuals."[3] In industry the effectiveness of engineers has been found to be limited by their lack of "people-wisdom," their reliance on "coldly rational judgment," and the recurrent appearance of a "noncommunicative syndrome."[4]

The president of a large corporation has said succinctly what many leaders of American industry have come to recognize as fact:

The specialist cannot function effectively at the top level of management if all he brings to it is his specialty. At that level, the daily problems call for broad general knowledge, open-mindedness, an understanding of human nature, an insight into human frailties, a fairness of mind, a clarity of thought . . . . The qualifications needed for leadership in industry are developed largely through a liberal arts education.[5]

The proposition has scarcely changed in the nineteen centuries since Vitruvius, the great Roman engineer, wrote that those who have acquired

> . . . skill without scholarship have never been able to reach a position of authority to correspond to their pains . . . . But those who have a thorough knowledge of both, like men armed at all points, have the sooner attained their object and carried authority with them.[6]

The good life

In addition to helping each of us to do his job more effectively—and of even greater importance in the last analysis—liberal learning yields great riches to the individual in pursuit of the good life. Knowledge and understanding provide pleasure that needs no practical justification. Beauty evokes joyousness that is its own reward. The most precious treasure awaiting the engineer in the world of the liberal arts is enrichment of his personal life—enrichment and the tranquility of spirit which accompanies new insight.

We engineers pride ourselves on being members of a profession which engages our energies and challenges our capacities. We are usually too much absorbed in our interesting work to be overly bothered by the doubts and anxieties which plague many of our less fortunate brethren. This concentration on work is a blessing, but it contains a hidden flaw. Our questioning and doubting are liable to be postponed, only to emerge in later years, sometimes with disturbing effect. It is better surely to expose oneself early and often to the eternal problems of philosophy and art than to be awakened with a start in one's waning years by the sudden asking of the questions, "What is life all about? What have I been living for?" Socrates' admonition still rings true. "The unconsidered life is not worth living."

Mark Van Doren has spoken of the happiness won by the

man who has sought inspiration and enlightenment in the "great tradition" of the liberal arts. "That happiness consists in the possession of his own powers, and in the sense that he has done all he could to avoid the bewilderment of one who suspects he has missed the main thing. There is no happiness like this."[7]

Status for the profession

As the individual engineer profits from acquaintance with the liberal arts, so will the entire profession. Our lack of "status," our unsatisfactory "image"—these are concerns which gnaw away at our collective professional contentment. Only a vastly increased number of liberally educated engineers can remedy this situation. Self-praising pronouncements emanating from our professional organizations surely will not suffice.

The public relations problems of the engineering profession are nothing new. They already existed in the days of ancient Greece. Xenophon spoke for most of his fellow citizens when he said that "the mechanical arts carry a social stigma and are rightly dishonored in our cities." Technologists, he maintained, "simply have not got the time to perform the offices of friendship or citizenship. Consequently they are looked upon as bad friends and bad patriots . . . ."[8]

A hundred years ago Ralph Waldo Emerson looked at the technologists of his day and spoke sadly of "great arts and little men." "Look up the inventors," he wrote. "Each has his own knack; his genius is in veins and spots. But the great, equal symmetrical brain, fed from a great heart, you shall not find."[9] Even Thomas Henry Huxley, nineteenth-century advocate of science and technology, expressed concern about technologists becoming "lopsided men." "The value of a cargo," he pointed out, "does not compensate for a ship's being out of trim."[10]

In the early twentieth century, engineering achieved a certain level of prestige, although the profession was still regarded warily even by its greatest admirers. Thus Thorstein Veblen in 1917:

> Popular sentiment in this country will not tolerate the assumption of responsibility by the technicians, who are in the popular apprehension conceived to be a somewhat fantastic brotherhood of over-specialized cranks, not to be trusted out of sight except under the restraining hand of safe and sane businessmen. Nor are the technicians themselves in the habit of taking a greatly different view of their own case.[11]

Today, when in the midst of spectacular engineering achievements, this galling tradition persists. An American science editor informs us that "the image that has been projected of the engineering profession—and images are very hard to change—is of a prejudiced, conservative, non-involved group."[12] An English science editor comments that engineers, "the men who daily make history, are still not accepted as important citizens! . . . . Even the word engineer has connotations of a man in a boiler suit who is a kind of modern blacksmith."[13] A public relations man captures the essence of a prevalent attitude in a few deft sentences:

> I grew up in the tradition of the engineer being a man with no verbal skills whatsoever. He was one of these guys who if you gave him an applied kind of problem would go off in a corner and work it out for you but, God forbid, don't ask him to explain it. He's no good with the English language; don't expect him to articulate himself. He is this kind of faceless, anonymous character.[14]

Engineers are certainly not insensitive to public opinion, nor do they engage in self-deception. A study has shown that "engineers themselves are convinced that the general public does not hold them in as great esteem as other professions."[15]

Only liberally educated engineers can bring the profession the esteem it craves and, in so many important ways, deserves. For one thing, only liberally educated engineers will possess the eloquence with which to impress upon their fellow citizens the inherent worth of engineering and its importance to society. It has been charged, and rightly so, that the engineering profession "has not been in touch with the people and by default has permitted a working partner (science) to capture the imagination of the nation."[16]

But there is a more important goal than "telling the story" of engineering to the public. If engineers themselves, as individuals, become truly cultured—that is, become educated in the liberal arts—then the word will spread without a "good press." If we engineers do not want to be known as "bad friends and bad patriots," "little men," "lopsided men," "overspecialized cranks," if we resent being characterized as a "prejudiced, conservative, noninvolved group," if we cringe at being looked at as "a kind of modern blacksmith," as "this kind of faceless, anonymous character," then it is up to us to make sure we resemble these things as little as possible. If engineers become increasingly wise, sensitive, humane, and responsible, we will not need public-relations techniques to sell us to the public.

The public good

And as the engineering profession gains prestige and authority, society as a whole will benefit. *For the world is desperately in need of the leadership that only engineers can give.* "The politicians, and even the statesmen," as James Reston of *The New York Times* has put it,

> . . . are merely scrambling to deal with the revolutions in weapons, agriculture and industry created by the scientists and the engineers. The latter have transformed man's capacity to give life, to sustain and prolong life, and to take life; and the politicians no longer find that they can deal with all the new complexities and ambiguities . . . .[17]

The world must listen to the engineer or it is doomed. Buckminster Fuller has stated the facts in the simplest terms:

> If humanity understood that the real world problem is that of upping the performances per pound of the world's metals and other resources, we might attempt to solve that problem deliberately, directly and efficiently . . . . But I find that approximately no one realizes what is going on. That is why we have been leaving it to the politician to make the world work. There is nothing political that the politician can do to make fewer resources do sixty percent more.[18]

We engineers already possess most of the technical knowledge required to provide food and shelter in abundance, restore purity to our air and water, heal the blight of our cities, untangle the snarl of traffic, harness our rivers, reap harvests from the oceans, husband our resources, and develop power from the sun and atom. We will—if the world will let us—subdue floods, minimize the danger from storms and earthquakes, and eventually control the weather. We will perform new miracles in the fields of medicine, communication, and transportation, and develop a continuous stream of marvelous fabrics and household appliances. We can—if called upon—contribute to the preservation of peace by assisting the underdeveloped nations and by devising improved means of arms control.

But unless we achieve a position of leadership, our talents will continue to be largely wasted and misdirected. The world will persist in demanding our blast furnaces but not our smoke-control devices, our highways but not our parks, our bombers but not our hospital ships. Running wild and out of control, technological progress will become a disease—a plague of asphalt and armaments, pollution and blight.

Admittedly, there is a school of thought which holds that the world's ills are not attributable to lack of leadership by the technologists, but rather to leadership heading in the wrong direction. "In every country in the world," according to George Orwell,

> . . . the large army of scientists and technicians, with the rest of us panting at their heels, are marching along the road of "progress" with the blind persistence of a column of ants. Comparatively few people want it to happen, plenty of people actively want it not to happen and yet it is happening. The process of mechanization has itself become a machine, a huge glittering vehicle whirling us we are not certain where, but probably toward the padded Wells-world and the brain in the bottle.[19]

"It is apparently our fate," echoes a French scholar, "to be facing a 'golden age' in the power of sorcerers who are totally blind to the meaning of the human adventure."[20]

Nor is this sentiment restricted to apprehensive artists and intellectuals. In his farewell address President Eisenhower warned the nation that its public policy might "become the captive of a scientific-technological elite." Senator Bartlett of Alaska has complained that "faceless technocrats in long, white coats are making decisions today which rightfully and by law should be made by the Congress."[21]

It is true that in government and industry engineers are numerically abundant and *potentially* powerful.[22] But the extent of our *actual* influence in directing the course of our society is a moot question indeed. In either case—whether the world is racing toward disaster in spite of us or because of us—clearly what is needed is enlightened engineering leadership.

Someone must step forward to say, "We can afford to make that automobile a little safer," "Let us build a factory that is more attractive," "Let us consider the possible harmful effects of that insecticide before we market it," "Let us develop a plant process that will not pollute the water we use," "Let us make that machine a little quieter," "Let us not demolish that historically precious old building," "Let us locate that dam, not only where it will generate the most power, but also where it will serve the interests of the community—esthetically, politically, and socially," "Let us build a rapid transit system for this city rather than a freeway that will bring more cars into an area already choked with traffic."

This "someone" cannot be an ordinary citizen of good will. He must be able to bolster his arguments with facts—technical, scientific, and economic. Hunches and sentiments will not be sufficient. His recommendations, in order to be persuasive, must be founded in a knowledge of resources, materials, and energy conversion; statistics, probabilities, and decision theory; computers, controls, and systems engineering. Moreover, this "someone" must be concerned. He must be articulate. He must be esteemed. And he must have a highly developed moral and esthetic sensibility. In short, he must be a liberally educated engineer.

Liberal education will not make prophets and saints out of engineers, and even if it did, this would not necessarily bring about instant Utopia. But this prudent qualification should not discourage us from moving in what we know to be the right direction.

The public philosophy

One thing further. A generation of liberally educated engineers would inevitably play an important role in the debates which are instrumental in shaping the public philosophy. Engineers are already developing techniques of decision making which will enable the leaders of society to choose rationally between alternative courses of action. When we are as wise as we are smart, we will be qualified to talk about new goals as well as methods, ultimate ends as well as means. We will have much of worth to contribute to the public philosophy, both in word and in deed.

Although world-wide conquest of poverty and need is far

from being achieved, the more developed nations are already encountering an entirely new spectrum of problems born of affluence. Future generations, having won the battle for survival, will be confronted with the task of maintaining vitality and pride in our communities, conquering boredom, and renewing faith in the inherent value of creative labor.

The response of truly civilized engineers could lead to a renaissance of engineering that would dazzle and inspire the world. In every nation, in every town, there would be a flowering of towers, arches, and domes; concert halls, stadiums, theatres, museums, and libraries; universities and art centers; memorials, shrines, and churches; parks, gardens, fountains, pools, arcades, and promenades. Treasures of antiquity would be recovered, preserved, and reconstructed. Research centers and sanctuaries would flourish in the deserts, the jungles, and on the polar ice, under the sea and in outer space. In all of this, every line, every proportion of structure, vehicle, and machine would spring, not from greed or grim necessity, as so much of it does today, but from an inner human striving for beauty and excellence. Lewis Mumford has spoken hopefully of the eventual coming of "a new technology, one so finely adjusted, so delicately responsive, that it will meet all the needs and occasions of life at a minimum cost of human values."[23] Such a technology will not be beyond the reach of engineers who have been steeped in the liberal arts.

With the coming of a civilized technology, the world will discover that engineering is not merely a means to an end, but rather an inherently worthy way of life. A revitalized and enlightened engineering will someday achieve its rightful place as one of the sublime enterprises of mankind. As historian Lynn White, Jr. has said,

> Technology is a profoundly spiritual form of thought. It has flourished best in the context of the Judaeo-Christian presup-

position that the physical universe was created for a good purpose, that it is not to be disregarded or transcended, but rather that, like the body itself, it is to be treasured and controlled as the necessary ground of psychic life.[24]

A recapitulation of reasons

These, then, are some of the reasons that we engineers should study the liberal arts:

1. To improve our intellectual competence and expand our imaginative powers.

2. To develop those qualities of character and personality which make for leadership and successful careers.

3. To enrich our personal lives with new knowledge and insight, with a keener appreciation of beauty.

4. To elevate the standards of our profession and to gain it increased esteem in our society.

5. To contribute to the public good—first, by using our improved status to see to it that our sensible technological advice is taken; second, by applying our enlarged wisdom and sensitivity, not only to the solution of engineering problems but also to the selection of worthy goals for our society; and third, by demonstrating to the world that technology can be more than a tool, can in itself be a revitalizing and profoundly beneficial force in human affairs.

What are the liberal arts?

In what has been said so far it has been assumed that we are all familiar with what is meant by a liberal education. And indeed we are, in a broad sense. Liberal learning, we know, concerns itself with the eternal quest for truth, goodness, and beauty. It grapples with such ultimate concerns as the meaning of justice, liberty, virtue, honor, love, and happiness. Its method is to study the works of scholars and artists, both past and present.

There are some who consider the ultimate purpose of liberal education to be the transmission of our cultural heritage and the creation of good citizens loyal to the ideals of our society. There are others who stress the development of the independent, sensitive, questioning mind, who see the liberal arts as having a critical, almost revolutionary, function. However, all agree that the ultimate goal of liberal learning is wisdom and a reverence for beauty.

Literally, arts that are "liberal" are those studies deemed fit for liberated, or free, men. In past ages only a few men were truly free; the vast majority lived as serfs, chained to soil they did not own. So liberal education has an aristocratic tradition. Because it was restricted to the upper classes, it came to serve the purpose of artificially defining the upper classes. This "snobbish" side of liberal learning becomes an anachronism in a democratic society. An engineering educator has put it this way:

> The *Oxford Dictionary* defines liberal education as education fit for a gentleman. That is still an acceptable definition; it is the idea of a gentleman which has changed . . . . Modern gentlemen do not belong to the leisured class. Many of them work something like a seventy-hour week . . . .[25]

In the universities of the Middle Ages there were established seven branches of liberal learning: grammar, logic, and rhetoric (in other words, literature and philosophy), and arithmetic, geometry, astronomy, and music (science and the fine arts). Through the years a liberal arts education has come to comprise all those studies which are not technical or vocational by nature, those which are not "useful arts." It is no longer said that the liberal arts are *for* free men. Instead one hears it said that the liberal arts *make* men free by liberating their minds from ignorance and dogma.

Liberal arts for the engineer

A truly liberal education includes the study of pure science and mathematics. In these fields the average engineer has received a considerable amount of instruction. Liberal learning also embraces the social sciences: sociology, anthropology, psychology, political science, economics, and the like. These are important and useful subjects, and no man can consider himself educated without some knowledge of them.

But when we say that engineers lack an adequate liberal arts education, we do not really mean that they need more training in the social sciences. For one thing, to the extent that engineers take liberal arts courses in college, they often select the social sciences, which appear to be more "useful" than such studies as, for example, literature. Also the social sciences, whatever their merits, have a certain "illiberal" quality about them. They are, after all, sciences, and their approach is essentially clinical. The social scientist is more a statistician than a philosopher. He is liable to make the engineer *more* "lopsided" rather than less.

We are left, then, with those subjects which constitute the true core of liberal learning: history, literature, philosophy, the fine arts, and music. These are the so-called *humanities* about which the average engineer has always known little and cared less. These are the subjects with which we must now try to gain some familiarity.

A world to be won

There is a world of wisdom and beauty to be won. Obviously, as busy engineers, we cannot explore more than the tiniest portion of it. But to explore even a tiny portion, to discover the coastal outlines and see the vistas, to touch in at port here and there is to change our lives for the good.

Our problem is not unlike that of the world traveler who is

constantly torn between the impulse to see as much as he can and the desire to linger in one spot in order to know it well. How much shall we survey in breadth and how much can we plumb in depth?

Certainly we want the overall view, superficial as it may be. Perspective and broad understanding are necessary first objectives. But the overall view becomes meaningless unless we stop here and there to investigate in detail, unless we find something to linger over and make our own. Each of us must seek his own balance between the general and the particular.

The problem of selecting particular works of literature and art from the myriads which surround us in this age of mass production is extremely vexing, almost paralyzing. Jacques Barzun has stated the problem well:

> The very bulk of the output kills appetite. Symphonies in bars and cabs, classical drama on television any day of the week, highbrow paperbacks in mountainous profusion (easier to buy than to read), "art seminars in the home," capsule operas, "Chopin by Starlight," "The Sound of Wagner," the Best of World Literature: this cornucopia thrust at the inexperienced and pouring out its contents over us all deadens attention and keeps taste stillborn, like any form of gross feeding. Too much art in too many places means art robbed of its right associations, its exact forms, its concentrated power. We are grateful for the comprehensive repertoire which modern industry for the first time puts within our reach, but we turn sick at the aggressive temptation, like the novice in the sweetshop.[26]

If we live in a sweetshop, we must learn discrimination and self-restraint. We must learn to relish the individual morsel without bewailing the fact that we cannot gorge ourselves. A single work of art, studied with love and understood well, may contain in microcosm and by implication as much as a thousand other works together. At least this must be our hope and our expectation, since we are busy professional men, and cannot delude ourselves into thinking that our experience in the arts can ever be comprehensive.

A further dilemma involves the question of whether we should be guided by what is said to be "worthwhile" or follow our own inclinations. We must do both, of course. Acknowledged masterpieces should not be foolishly ignored; we cannot rely exclusively on our taste, which is, after all, also our ignorance and prejudice. But neither must we follow the herd. Our taste should be challenged, refined, and stretched, but never overwhelmed. Ultimately it must prevail. We are under no obligation to worship unthinkingly at old and musty shrines.

Apologetic or proud?

And this brings us to the question of how we, as engineers, should best approach the liberal arts. Should we come hat in hand, ashamed, apologetic, and willing to be melted down and molded anew? Or should we come proudly, willing to grow, but only with the understanding that we start from what we *are*? Eric Ashby, author of *Technology and the Academics*, leaves no doubt about the course to be taken. "The path to culture should be through a man's specialism, not by by-passing it . . . . The *sine qua non* for a man who desires to be cultured is a deep and enduring enthusiasm to do one thing excellently."[27]

Unless the liberal arts can be approached *through engineering* they will seem lifeless and frivolous to those of us who are professional engineers. Engineering educators are grappling with this problem now. They are agreed that liberal education for engineers is essential, but they are fearful of having it degenerate into mere "appreciation" or "ornamentation."

Five bridges to be crossed

The approach in this book will be to seek a bridge between engineering and each of the five subjects to be considered. From such a bridge we can look back over our own profession and ahead to the new world to be explored, observing the similarities of terrain, and discerning the common ground on which all worthy human endeavor rests. There is much talk these days about building bridges between the two cultures. These bridges do not so much require building as discovering; they already exist.

One such bridge has been discovered only recently and it is being enthusiastically reconstructed at this time. It is at the frontier where engineering and history meet, and it is called "the history of technology."

A bridge between engineering and literature has long been sought, and I think rather fruitlessly, in such desert areas as "engineers as writers" and "report writing for engineers." Here an attempt will be made to explore a new and unmapped territory, "the engineer as a protagonist in fiction."

Across the gulf between engineering and philosophy is suspended "the truth of science," a fragile structure, scarcely known to most engineers, although it is well traveled by many scientists and philosophers.

Engineering and the fine arts are joined by the age-old link of utility and beauty, often crossed by architects and designers but all too seldom by engineers.

Between engineering and music we find "sound as environment," a span which lately is attracting attention from people in many disciplines.

Let us together venture upon these bridges, and then let us cross them into the alluring lands which lie beyond. We may enter these new lands as relative strangers, but we will know who we are, why we have come, and the route we have traveled. With this sense of confidence and purpose we may soon find ourselves very much at ease in our new surroundings. The liberal arts, after all, have nourished and delighted men since the beginning of civilization.

For the engineer who doubts the value of a liberal arts education, an eye-opening book is Robert A. Goldwin and Charles A. Nelson (eds.), *Toward the Liberally Educated Executive* (Mentor Books MD 299). This slim volume includes essays by prominent educators, businessmen, and creative artists, all directed toward the practical and personal benefits to be gained in a liberal education. Particularly interesting is a report on programs in liberal education for executives conducted by the Bell Telephone Company. An appendix lists institutions of higher education which conduct special programs for industry, and also provides book lists used in many of these programs.

A beautiful and inspiring work is Mark Van Doren, *Liberal Education* (Beacon Press BP 86).

From the point of view of the professional educator, an interesting and useful book is Edwin J. Holstein and Earl J. McGrath, *Liberal Education and Engineering* (Teachers College, Columbia University, 1960).

An excellent, informal history of engineering education, shedding much light on the sociological background of the profession, is Eric Ashby, *Technology and the Academics* (Macmillan Papermac 43).

A work of historic importance, a "must" for the reader interested in the interrelationship between technology and the liberal arts, is C. P. Snow, *The Two Cultures and a Second Look* (Mentor Books MP 557).

A unique and provocative anthology: W. H. Davenport and D. Rosenthal (eds.), *Engineering—Its Role and Function in Human Society* (EDP Report No. 3-66, University of California, Los Angeles).

Don K. Price, *The Scientific Estate* (Harvard University Press, 1965) is a fascinating book which tells of the engineer's place in the power structure of our nation. Jay M. Gould, *The*

Technical Elite (Augustus M. Kelley, 1966) contains much enlightening statistical information about the rise of engineers in industry. Of historical interest is Thorstein Veblen, *The Engineers and the Price System* (Harbinger Books HO31).

Two statements of interest to the thoughtful citizen are Jacques Barzun, *The House of Intellect* (Harper Torchbooks TB 1051) and John W. Gardner, *Excellence* (Harper Colophon Books CN3H).

CHAPTER TWO

The Bridge
to History:
The History
of Technology

One generalization that can safely be made about engineers is that we are forward-looking. We are, one might say, in love with the future and very little interested in the past. Undeniably this outlook is an asset in our work; it helps us produce more efficiently, just as blinders help a horse pull his wagon more steadily in traffic.

But, for the sake of our competence in the long run—to say nothing of our satisfaction and self-respect—an awareness of the past is a good and necessary thing for us to have. At the very least we should have an awareness of our *own* past, the history of our profession and its works.

Technology as a dominant historical force

To the extent that we think of history at all, engineers are inclined to assume that technology is a dominant historical force. This assumption is the source of a rather pleasant measure of professional pride. Of course technology is not identical with engineering, and not all technological accomplishments can be credited to engineers. Craftsmen, technicians, and plain tinkerers have made notable contributions, and in modern times so have scientists. But the history of technology is close enough to being the history of engineering for the engineer to feel possessive toward it. And feeling possessive, he has reason to feel proud.

The most crucial changes in human affairs seem to be associated intimately with technological advances; or, more to the point, they seem to have been *made possible* by such advances. The ability to mine and work metals, to mold pottery and weave textiles, to construct buildings and bridges and dams, to devise means of transportation and communication, to harness water, wind, and steam—each new achievement has served to trigger spectacular advances in civilization. We speak of the Stone Age, the Bronze Age, the Iron Age, the Industrial Revolution, the Scientific Revolution, and so forth, tacitly acknowledging the pervasive influence of technology in history.

In 1874, Samuel Smiles, author of *Lives of the Engineers,* asked; "Are not the men who have made the motive power of the country, and immensely increased its productive strength, the men above all others who have tended to make the country what it is?"[1]

A contemporary historian of engineering proclaims flatly, "The engineer has been, and is, a maker of history."[2] Another puts it this way: "Even with the earliest peoples at the dawn of history, the periods of economic and cultural prosperity are closely associated with, and indeed dependent on, the high standard of technical knowledge."[3] Still another makes this sweeping statement:

> Civilization, as we know it today, owes its existence to the engineers. These are the men who, down the long centuries, have learned to exploit the properties of matter and the sources of power for the benefit of mankind. By an organized, rational effort to use the material world around them, engineers devised the myriad comforts and conveniences that mark the difference between our lives and those of our fore-fathers thousands of years ago.
>
> The story of civilization is, in a sense, the story of engineering—that long and arduous struggle to make the forces of nature work for man's good.[4]

In many fine books the engineer can read with pleasure of his profession's formative role in history. He can learn how miracles of irrigation engineering allowed Egypt and Mesopotamia to develop great civilizations, how the ascendance of Athens depended in great measure on the amazing silver mines of Mount Laurion, how Roman roads and aqueducts made possible a mighty empire, and so on right up to the present era of automation and nuclear energy.

Marshall McLuhan, one of the more celebrated intellectuals of the day, maintains that a major shift in a society's predominant technology of communication is "the crucially determining force behind social changes, initiating great transformations not only in social organization but human sensibilities."[5]

Is engineering indeed the key to history, the controlling factor in the rise of civilizations? And should not the answer to this question be of paramount interest to every engineer?

Upon reflection, it can be seen that the tidy linking of technological cause to historical effect is a gross oversimplification. The authors of *Engineering in History* take a more cautious view. "Engineering advance is vital," they note, "as one of the interdependent variables on which the evolution of history depends . . . . Engineering by itself is not enough; it must be integrated with other knowledge and directed by ethical principles."[6]

Technology and science

To begin with, engineering must be integrated with scientific knowledge. Technological progress without compensating scientific progress can be disastrous to a society. Take, for example, the improvement in pumping equipment which made it possible for the engineer to supply water to cities from nearby sources without having to bring it in by gravity over long and costly aqueducts. The engineering accomplishment was remarkable, but until the theory of the germ origin of infectious disease became known, engineers, in innocence, and in ignorance, caused innumerable fatalities by supplying polluted drinking water to urban centers.

It is worth pausing for a moment to consider the interesting and complex historical relationship between science and engineering. In these days of close scientific and engineering cooperation we are inclined to forget that for many hundreds of years science and engineering went their separate ways as if neither had anything to contribute to, or learn from, the other. From earliest times engineers were proud and independent craftsmen who were guided in their work not by scientific theories but by common sense and by practical rules gleaned from experience. Scientific speculation and research developed along completely independent lines, and even the great scientific and mathematical advances of the seventeenth century— the age of Bacon, Galileo, Leibniz, and Newton—were not applied to contemporary engineering tasks. It was not until the eighteenth century that engineers first looked to science for solutions to problems of structures and hydraulics. As late as 1822 a prominent English engineer could remark that "the stability of a building is inversely proportional to the science of the builder."[7]

But once the courtship began, a wedding was inevitable; science and engineering simply had too much to offer each other for it to be otherwise. More and more they have become interdependent, and one is now practically unthinkable without the other. Engineering has come to rely on scientific theory as a basic tool of design, and science looks to engineering for its instruments, its working models, and, in general, the adaptation of scientific findings for society's use. In some areas science darts far ahead, making discoveries for which no practical application is apparent. Conversely, engineers, like doctors, often make use of procedures which "work," although the scientific reasons for success are not yet completely understood. But, in the main, science and engineering must progress side by side if either is to have a maximum positive effect in history.

Both engineering and science are popularly considered to be tools of conquest, enabling man to extend his control over his environment. This is certainly true, but they also affect history in a less obvious but no less potent manner by changing the ways in which men think. Technological and scientific accomplishments have usually had the effect of boosting morale, making men increasingly confident of their ability to master nature and almost belligerent in their anxiety to get on with the job. The Age of Reason, as we shall see in the next chapter, was born in the rush of enthusiasm and optimism that followed hard on the heels of the great scientific discoveries of Newton and his contemporaries in the seventeenth century.

On the other hand, scientific discoveries have also had a strangely demoralizing influence ever since Copernicus first deprived man of his favored spot in the heavens. Darwin subsequently showed him that he was just another animal, and today's scientists are well on their way to convincing him that he is simply a conglomeration of electromagnetic impulses, an insignificant speck in an incredibly immense universe. Be this as it may (and we will return to the philosophical implications of science and technology in later chapters), scientific achievement is clearly an essential ingredient of a high civilization.

Technology and agriculture

In addition to science, there are other kinds of knowledge which a society must possess in order for its technology to prove effective. Foremost amongst these is the knowledge of agricultural techniques. Nomadic tribes of preagricultural times showed great ingenuity and engineering ability. They manufactured spears, axes, fishhooks, bows and arrows, canoes, skis, sleds, and other skillfully conceived appliances. But until the development of agriculture and animal husbandry, these clever technologists remained at the mercy of the uncertain supply of wild game. They lived at a bare subsistence level and were unable to afford the luxury of any activity not directly related to the fulfilling of basic bodily needs. The development of any civilization is clearly dependent on the ability of a few to grow food for the many, and without skilled farmers there can be no industry and no engineering worthy of the name. Engineers can contribute much to agricultural efficiency through improvement of farm implements, development of chemicals, and extension of irrigation. Scientists can help as well. But in the end it is the farmers who must sow the seed and reap the harvest upon which the entire community subsists. In today's world the leaders of Communist China are among those who are discovering how difficult it is to expand industrially when agricultural problems remain unsolved.

Technology and government

Even when engineering skill is integrated with scientific competence and agricultural efficiency, history shows us that success is not assured. Another form of knowledge is required which, for want of a better definition, we can call the knowledge of government. Organization, cooperation, and self-discipline are prerequisites for an orderly and functioning community, and outside the bounds of such a community the finest engineering talent is ineffectual. France was the first nation to successfully combine science and engineering, and it followed that in the eighteenth century French engineering was the envy of the civilized world. But eighteenth-century France was politically bankrupt, and when she fell prey to the fury of her revolution, it was little England who stepped forward as the master technologist. Political stability was one of the crucial attributes which enabled England to snatch the torch from the hand of a convulsed France and to dominate the world of industry and commerce for more than a century.

Of course political stability, when dependent upon an ultra-conservative political tradition, can stifle creative engineering effort. We have seen much evidence of this in the Orient and in Africa, where the currents of superstition and apathy run strong. We have also seen, particularly in Latin America, that corrupt and greedy groups who see their interests best served by keeping the masses in poverty and ignorance can obstruct the most critically needed public improvements.

In fact, the deeper we probe into the influence of political traditions on technology, the more we encounter disconcerting paradoxes. We find that England, after several generations of unchallenged technological supremacy, lost much of its forward momentum because of hallowed prejudices which rated a career in industry low on the social scale. If a man was able to make his fortune in industry he usually did all in his power to see to it that his sons studied the classics and went on to a more esteemed career in the government, the army, or the church. In the United States of America, on the other hand, inventiveness and ingenuity were much admired, and success in industry was a means of achieving social prominence. In this climate technology flourished. Oddly enough, technology also flourished in Germany in the late nineteenth century in spite of, or rather because of, an almost feudal social structure. Since class barriers were *more* impregnable than they were in England, German families were content to develop industries for generation after generation without thought of social "improvement" gained by changing occupations. This same stratification of classes helped to develop the proud and skilled craftsmen of the medieval guilds.

Obviously there are many subtle nuances in the interrelationship between social tradition and engineering success. But there can be no question about the basic premise: only in an orderly community can there be significant technological progress.

Technology and ethical principles

A science, an agriculture, and a government—these, then, are some of the things a community must possess if its technology is to flourish. There are others, of course, not the least important of which is skill in trade and finance. But this array of assets, even together with engineering genius, will not suffice to guarantee a flourishing society. There still remains that intangible quality which the authors of *Engineering in History* identify as "ethical principles." This topic is worthy of volumes, but perhaps a few briefly considered examples will serve our present purpose.

Slavery existed as an accepted institution throughout most of recorded history, and there is little evidence to indicate that engineers were dissatisfied with this primary source of power. Are we, then, to credit engineers with abolishing slavery by discovering new sources of energy in nature? Or was it, perhaps, mankind's dissatisfaction with forced servitude that created a climate of opinion in which the engineer was obliged to develop new

sources of power? Did the engineer give the idea to the moralist
or was it the other way around? Have advances in sanitation
technology brought about an increased concern for individual
life, or did the change in values precede the improvement in
skills? Sometimes it seems as if society commissions the accomplishment of engineering feats the way a patron commissions
his protégé to produce a work of art. The patron lacks creative
talent; but the protégé needs someone to guide him, to under-
write his efforts, and to appreciate what he does. If the patron
has bad taste and a closed mind, there is not much that the
protégé can do about it.

Certainly when a society's aims are misdirected, its historical
destiny is largely beyond the engineer's control. Nazi Germany
boasted many fine engineering accomplishments, but its odious
ambitions contained the seeds of self-destruction. Innumerable
warrior tribes have raced across the pages of history, and many
of them, on the evidence of their great skill in designing and
fabricating weapons of war, must be ranked high in engineering
ability. But where adequate moral goals have been lacking,
technological competence has usually been wasted. Some nations, although not necessarily more wicked than others, have
squandered their energies in nonfruitful ways. For example,
Spain, one of the earliest and greatest of the maritime explorer
nations, foolishly concentrated on the seeking, mining, and
hoarding of gold, while others were more prudently colonizing
and developing industry.

The good have not always prospered nor the evil been
afflicted, and the present state of the world hardly makes one
overly optimistic about the future. But reviewing the course of
history, we can see, dimly perhaps, that an increasingly close
alliance developed between technological progress and morally
worthy goals. Clearly virtue cannot prevail without competence;
neither is it likely, if history is to be believed, that competence
can prevail without some measure of virtue. Upon reflection, the

role of the engineer in history turns out to be crucial but not self-sufficient. One can only conclude that both society and engineers stand to benefit by the wholesome integration of technology into the total social organism.

The history of technology

Having considered generally the role of technology in history, let us now review some of the specific technological developments which have been significant in the evolution of civilizations. These inventions, discoveries, methods, and processes grew out of a rich soil of genius and luck, intuition and experiment, energy and diligence, ambition and need. Behind each advance there is a remarkable story, and it is these stories that are now being rediscovered and retold, woven into the fabric of the new history of technology. Why have they been neglected for so long? Because, suggests historian Lynn White, Jr., in the past, education and culture were dominated by an aristocracy to whom technology was only of marginal interest.[8] Looked at in this way, current interest in the history of technology is a product of democracy.

Each advance listed below, in addition to being a dramatic technological achievement, had spectacular social, political, and cultural ramifications. These also are part of the tale that the history of technology unfolds.

A mere list of these milestones of human progress is exciting to read. One conjures up first the achievement itself, then the process of discovery, and finally the impact it had on society. In one sense the list tells a story which requires very little commentary. We simply *know* the effect on civilization of the clock, and printing, and gunpowder, and steam power. In another sense the list tells a story worthy of a lifetime of commentary. To engineers, what follows is a family tree and a legacy, an inspiration and a challenge—a challenge not only to build upon the past, but to study that past as well.

Landmarks in the history
of technology[9]

B.C.

ca. 4000   Irrigation works control flooding of the Nile, the
Tigris and Euphrates, and the Indus rivers, making
possible agriculture adequate to support the growth
of civilizations.

ca. 3500   First evidence of copper tools and wheeled vehicles
in Egypt and the Near East.

ca. 3000   Pottery making on the wheel.

ca. 2500   The Great Pyramid of Cheops. Sailing ships.

ca. 2000   Bronze in use. By alloying copper with tin, a harder
and less malleable metal is developed. Bronze is also
more fusible than copper, and is thus better suited
for casting.

ca. 1800   Horse-drawn chariots become "a decisive factor both
in the great wars between the ancient empires and
in the upkeep of internal communications upon
which their survival depended."[10]

ca. 1500   The shadow clock appears in Egypt.

ca. 1300   Glass vessels manufactured in Egypt.

ca. 1000   Iron tools and weapons; the beginning of the Iron
Age.

ca. 450   The flowering of civilization in Greece. The mining
of silver was in part responsible for the wealth of
Athens. Greek ascendance in the Mediterranean also
owed much to Greek skill in building harbors. Although they held technology in low esteem, the
Greeks pioneered in tunnel building and city planning. They were peerless architects and accomplished builders.

ca. 250   Parchment is manufactured in Pergamum, Asia
Minor, providing a tougher and more lasting writing
surface than Egyptian papyrus.

ca. 200   Glass blowing develops in Syria and then spreads rapidly throughout the Roman world.

A.D.

ca. 100   The Roman Empire at its height, serviced by a network of extraordinary roads, bridges and aqueducts, from Spain and North Africa all through Europe and into Asia Minor. The Romans inherited the arch from the Etruscans and developed its construction to a fine art. They made extensive use of natural cement (pozzuolana), and were accomplished brick masons. Although not particularly inventive, they exploited the basic knowledge they inherited from others, and developed the art of construction to a height not equalled again for a thousand years. Among other technological achievements of this period are the utilization of water wheels and the manufacture of brass.

ca. 700   Chinese methods of papermaking learned by Arabs, later to be introduced by them, through Spain, to Europe.

ca. 750   The stirrup is introduced in Europe, making heavy-shock mounted combat possible. "Few inventions have been so simple as the stirrup, but few have had so catalytic an influence in history. The requirements of the new mode of warfare which it made possible found expression in a new form of western European society dominated by an aristocracy of warriors endowed with land so that they might fight in a new and highly specialized way."[11]

ca. 800   Modern horse harness in Europe, enabling horses to pull a load four or five times heavier than they could with the older choking harness. This portends great benefits for agriculture and transportation.

ca. 1000   The magnetic compass, long known to the Chinese, comes to Europe.

ca. 1100   The windmill, known in Persia as early as 600, appears in Europe. "Thanks to the menial services of wind and water, a large intelligentsia could come into existence, and great works of art and scholarship and science and engineering could be created without recourse to slavery: a release of energy, a victory for the human spirit."[12]

ca. 1298   The spinning wheel appears in Europe via India.

ca. 1324   The use of cannon spells the doom of armor and castles, and indeed of feudalism itself. It also spurs interest in metallurgy and surveying.

ca. 1370   The mechanical clock is perfected. "The regular striking of the bells brought a new regularity into the life of the workman and the merchant. The bells of the clock tower almost defined urban existence. Time-keeping passed into time-serving and time-accounting and time-rationing. As this took place, Eternity ceased gradually to serve as the measure and focus of human actions. The clock, not the steam-engine, is the key-machine of the modern industrial age."[13]

ca. 1450   Gutenberg's printing press is a major factor in disseminating the "new learning" of the Renaissance, and marking the change from an oral culture to one depending on the written word. No longer will books belong exclusively to the church and the privileged few. At this time the great voyages of exploration begin, made possible by the mariner's compass, the fixed rudder, and striking advances in ship design. The Renaissance is also notable for the development of the canal lock and advances in dome construction.

ca. 1500   Leonardo da Vinci invents the centrifugal pump, the universal joint, the conical screw, link chains, spiral gears, and many other devices. Other inventions of the sixteenth century include the portable watch with mainspring (1500), the foot-driven spinning wheel (1530), the screw lathe (1578), and the compound microscope (1590), a key to the coming blossoming of science and medicine.

1600   The date usually given as the beginning of the era of modern science. This is the century of Francis Bacon (the scientific method), Galileo (modern astronomy and the pendulum), Leibniz (differential calculus), and Newton (the laws of gravitation).

1660   Beginning of the reign of Louis XIV in France. The Age of Reason. French engineers, established in national public-works departments and professional schools, bring the art of stone-masonry arch bridges to perfection. They also develop the cofferdam and make great strides in hydraulics. During the next one hundred years engineering science gradually comes into being, as the engineers of France begin to turn away from the old empiricism and to seek guidance from science.

1750   The date usually given as the beginning of the Industrial Revolution. Life in the Western world begins to change at a dizzying pace.

New materials make possible the development of fabulous structures and machines. Commercial manufacture of crucible steel dates from 1751. In 1756 Smeaton manufactures cement, and by 1824 Portland cement is being produced. In 1839 Goodyear develops the hot vulcanization of rubber. By 1856 we have Bessemer's steel converter and

Siemens's open-hearth furnace. In the 1880s aluminum is being produced commercially.

Textiles are mass-produced by the spinning machine (1767), Cartwright's power loom (1785), Whitney's cotton gin (1793), and Howe's sewing machine (1845).

Agriculture is revolutionized by McCormick's reaping machine (1831) and other devices, making possible a tremendous growth in population.

Transportation shrinks the globe. After Cugnot's steam carriage (1769), we have Fulton's steamboat (1803), Hancock's steam automobile (1827), the Liverpool-Manchester railway (1830), the Great Eastern steamship (1853), and Henry Ford's gasoline motor car (1892–1903). The Montgolfiers fly their balloon in 1783, and the Wrights their airplane in 1903.

Advances in communications put man in instantaneous contact with his fellows all over the world and change man's conception of his environment in ways that we are still struggling to comprehend. After the electric telegraph (1835), we have Bell's telephone (1876), Edison's microphone and phonograph (1877), Marconi's radio telegraph (1896), radio broadcasting (1920), and television (mass-produced starting in 1946). From the daguerreotype (1839) there evolves Eastman's camera (1886) and Edison's motion pictures (1893).

Underlying all is the development of new sources of power. Newcomen had invented a steam engine as early as 1705, but it is not until 1776 that Watt's steam engine is put to use. Barnett invents his gasoline engine in 1838, and by the 1890s we have the Diesel engine. Volta's galvanic cell dates from 1800, Faraday's dynamo from 1831, and Edison's first central power station from 1882.

The Industrial Revolution has freed millions of men from onerous labor, and bestowed upon them untold luxuries. At the same time it has confronted them with a whole new spectrum of social, economic, and political problems which they have not yet begun to solve.

1945   The start of the Atomic Age, which might equally well be labeled the Space Age, the Age of Automation, or the Age of the Computer. The technological means are now at hand to provide comfort and security for all men—or to destroy completely the civilization which we have so painstakingly created.

Recommended reading

An ideal introductory work is Thomas Parke Hughes (ed.), *The Development of Western Technology Since 1500* (Macmillan 35845). This slim anthology contains an instructive introduction, a provocative essay by Lewis Mumford on the social consequences of technology, and fourteen selections covering the Renaissance (one on Leonardo da Vinci), the seventeenth and eighteenth centuries, the Industrial Revolution, and nineteenth-century technology. All the essays are brief and interesting; they are contributed by notable men in the field—some contemporary and some from earlier times.

For technology prior to 1500, try Lynn White, Jr., *Medieval Technology and Social Change* (Oxford Paperbacks No. 79). This is a work of scholarship, chock-full of footnotes; but it contains some fascinating facts and original observations about the effects of technological innovations on the course of Western civilization.

A classic in the field, which traces the origins of technology back to the beginnings of mankind, is Lewis Mumford, *Technics and Civilization* (Harbinger Books HO30). Mumford is a philosopher as well as a historian, and he delves deeply into the effect of technological advance on the cultural and psychological well-being of man. His conclusions are disturbing. His erudition is impressive. This is not a book that one glides through quickly, but Mumford is one author with whom every engineer should have an acquaintance. Perhaps this acquaintance should first be made through the shorter *Art and Technics,* recommended in Chapter 8.

The most complete one-volume work in this field is T. K. Derry and Trevor I. Williams, *A Short History of Technology from the Earliest Times to A.D. 1900* (Oxford University Press, 1961). Technically this book of almost eight hundred pages tells the whole story; socially it does not probe deep for causes or effects. It is called "short" because it is a successor to the five-volume *History of Technology* published by Oxford University Press in 1954–57.

A comprehensive two-volume text is Melvin Kranzberg and Carroll W. Pursell, Jr. (eds.), *Technology in Western Civilization* (Oxford University Press, 1967).

A valuable work, consisting mainly of writings by and about technologists from antiquity on, is Friedrich Klemm, *The History of Western Technology* (M.I.T. 14). The eye-witness accounts of people, both technical and nontechnical, who actually experienced the effects of changing technology make this a fascinating book to browse through.

For those interested in the very beginnings of things: Kenneth P. Oakley, *Man the Tool-Maker* (Phoenix Books P20) and V. Gordon Childe, *Man Makes Himself* (Mentor Books MP 384).

To turn from technology in general to engineering in particular, we should mention first James Kip Finch, a respected authority whose *Engineering and Western Civilization* (McGraw-Hill, 1951) is a well-established text. Available in paperback is his *The Story of Engineering* (Anchor Books A214). Other authoritative works are Kirby, Withington, Darling, and Kilgour, *Engineering in History* (McGraw-Hill, 1956); Hans Straub, *A History of Civil Engineering* (M.I.T. 18); and W. H. G. Armytage, *A Social History of Engineering* (Pitman, 1961). For pleasurable reading: L. Sprague de Camp, *The Ancient Engineers* (Doubleday, 1963), is tops. Its title does not really do it justice, since it carries the story of engineering into the Renaissance.

Other recommended works devoted to special topics: H. J. Habakkuk, *American and British Technology in the Nineteenth Century* (Oxford University Press, 1962); L. Sprague de Camp, *The Heroic Age of American Invention* (Doubleday, 1961); Abbott Payson Usher, *A History of Mechanical Inventions,* (Beacon Press BP84); L. T. C. Rolt, *A Short History of Machine Tools* (M.I.T. 19); Roger Burlingame, *March of the Iron Men* (Universal Library 74); John Stover, *American Railroads* (University of Chicago 20); John Roe, *The American Automobile* (University of Chicago, 1965); Theodore A. Wertime, *The Coming of the Age of Steel* (University of Chicago, 1962); Harold Sharlin, *The Making of the Electrical Age* (Abelard, 1963); David B. Steinman and Sara Ruth Watson, *Bridges and Their Builders* (Dover Paperbacks). For illustrations: Umberto Eco and G. B. Zorzoli, *Picture History of Inventions* (Macmillan, 1963); *Machines* (Life Science Library, Time, Inc., 1964); Robert Soulard, *A History of the Machine* (Hawthorn Books, 1963); A. G. Keller, *A Theatre of Machines* (Macmillan, 1965).

The history of science is an appropriate supplement to the history of technology. Three enjoyable introductory works are

James Jeans, *The Growth of Physical Science* (Premier Books D70); Herbert Butterfield et al., *A Short History of Science* (Anchor Books A180); William Cecil Dampier, *A Shorter History of Science* (Meridian Books M47). A two-volume combined history is Robert J. Forbes and E. J. Dijksterhuis, *History of Science and Technology* (Penguin Books A498 and A499).

An outstanding biography is Matthew Josephson, *Edison* (McGraw-Hill 33046). Samuel Smiles' well-known nineteenth-century paean of praise to British engineers, *Lives of the Engineers* has been reissued (M.I.T., 1966).

Marshall McLuhan, as we have briefly noted, has propounded some startling theories about how changes in communications technology radically reshape the very quality of our lives. Acclaimed as a genius and condemned as a charlatan, this controversial professor figures to be an important feature of our intellectual landscape in the years ahead. Try his *Understanding Media* (McGraw-Hill 45436), and Edmund Carpenter and Marshall McLuhan (eds.), *Explorations in Communication: An Anthology* (Beacon Press BP218).

The study of the history of technology is in its infancy, and every year new and important works will be forthcoming. To keep abreast of this vital and increasingly important subject engineers can do no better than to join The Society for the History of Technology and thereby subscribe to the superb quarterly, *Technology and Culture*. (Address: Journals Division, The University of Chicago Press.)

This is one field—perhaps the only one to be discussed in this book—of which it can be said with some assurance that the best is yet to come.

CHAPTER THREE

The World
of History

The history of technology leads us straight into the great world of history itself. For how can we study weapons and not wars, ships and not voyages, railroads and not empires, cathedrals and not popes?

Yet, it might be argued, the history of technology is a serious business, interesting and valuable to engineers, whereas the rest of history is simply an idle pastime, "merely gossip" in Oscar Wilde's phrase, "bunk" as Henry Ford so bluntly put it.

Two hundred years ago Voltaire, who was a noted historian himself, wrote what might be considered a classic statement of the engineer's jaundiced view of history:

It always takes more pains and application to look into, let us say, the kind of machine that could provide Paris with plenty of water—which we surely need; whereas all one has to do in order to learn the old wives' tales handed down to us under the name of history is to open one's eyes and read. These tales are told over and over again, even though they do not much matter to us.[1]

Naturally Voltaire was only referring to history as it was written by others than himself. In his own historical writings he proposed to record "that which merits the attention of the ages . . . that which depicts the genius and manners of men, or which serves to instruct and inculcate the love of country, of virtue, and of art."[2]

Although history may at first glance appear frivolous when compared with technology, it has an importance of its own. Voltaire knew this, and it would be unwise for us, as engineers, to overlook it.

The uses of history

Most historians are agreed that the first purpose of history is to educate. Surely much practical good can result if men learn of the mistakes of the past in order to avoid repeating them, and of the triumphs, in order to emulate them.

In addition to educating, history should, in the words of the great English historian, Trevelyan, "breed enthusiasm." The dreams and achievements of earlier ages can inspire us in public and in private life. A strictly contemporary view of the world is impoverishing. "The ideals of no one epoch can in themselves be sufficient as an interpretation of life."[3]

Then, of course, there is the pleasure—the pure pleasure of reading about the past. History has been called a pageant, and to the reader of history it sometimes seems as if this pageant has been created by a masterful storyteller for our amazement and entertainment.

A study of history can give us education and inspiration and pleasure, and one thing more—a sense of our common past (our *heritage* if you will), a sense of "belonging," of being joined with our fellow men in a great adventure. A knowledge of history is as vital as citizenship and as important as a family name.

Theories of history

To agree that knowledge of history is a desirable end only brings us face to face with the question, "Of what precisely ought history to consist?" Clearly by "history" we mean the record of past events. But this only defines the historian's problem; it does not begin to solve it. Is he to tell us of battles and treaties or constitutions and customs, of plagues and migrations or fables and songs? Is he to deal in days or decades? Is he to tell of men or masses?

The selection of *what* to tell is simplicity itself compared with the next step, which is to ascertain *why* it came to pass. There are almost as many theories of history as there are historians, which is certainly a clear indication that history is more an art than a science.

One dispute of long standing concerns the influence of individuals on events. Do extraordinary men such as Napoleon and Churchill mold their ages or are they merely swept along by obscure and irresistible historical forces? Are there laws which govern the rise and fall of civilizations, or does blind chance play a deciding role? Do hospitable terrain and abundant natural resources automatically contribute to a society's prosperity, or are better results to be expected from those who have encountered what Toynbee calls "the virtues of adversity?"

Several biologists have sought to show that the growth of societies is governed by much the same processes as is the growth of living organisms. There have been interesting and persuasive scientific accounts of the effects of climate and soil on civilizations. Other studies have traced the effects of public health as a controlling historical factor. One theory has it that the fall of the Roman Empire was brought about by an endemic disease which debilitated the populace.

It was fashionable not so many years ago to assume that the raw economic needs of men provided the key to historical understanding. Then the pendulum swung, and interest reverted to the influence of "ideas," of religious beliefs and cultural mores. Technology and science, as we have seen, play a crucial role, perhaps second to none.

The answer is, of course, that there is no particular theory of history that is absolutely true; there is no particular group of facts that can recreate the essence of a past era. The search for the past is a never-ending approximation, a continual process of selection and insight. As Jacques Barzun has said, "to put intellectual order in place of the intelligible disorder of history is to apply the geometrical spirit to a subject that calls for the spirit of finesse."[4]

A few significant facts

There is, however, a basic skeleton, a bare minimum of generally agreed-upon significant facts from which all understanding and discussion of history must begin. It is this bare minimum which must be our first objective.

What follows is a brief review of the history of the Western world from earliest times up to the beginnings of the modern age. (The Orient, too, has a history very much worth studying, but first let us seek our own roots.) Men who have tried to incorporate such an historical review in a volume, or even in several volumes, have filled more pages with apologies than can be devoted here to the entire subject. So apologies can be taken for granted and will not be spelled out. The purpose here is to acquaint the engineer with the main periods of history—"re-acquaint" would be more accurate, for all of us have studied history at some time in our lives, and hardly anything that follows will be *new* knowledge to the reader. As elsewhere in this book it is hoped that a few essential facts will refresh the memory, fill in some blank spaces, pique the curiosity, and result in new respect for an alien field and a desire to study it in whatever depth time permits.

Prehistory

The earliest manlike creatures appeared on the earth perhaps two million years ago. About three hundred thousand years ago, having already discovered fire, men began to make rudimentary stone tools. This step marks the beginning of the Paleolithic (or Old Stone) Age. Through thousands of generations these men of prehistory roamed the earth in small family and tribelike groups. Hunters they were, dependent upon the chase for survival, and they followed the herds of game, whose movements in turn were controlled by the available water and vegetation and by the comings and goings of the polar ice caps.

Although most of our information about prehistoric man comes to us through findings of stone tools, there is increasing evidence that his life was rich in spiritual overtones. He buried his dead with care, and tens of thousands of years ago he decorated his caves with paintings showing great artistic and religious feeling.

When the ice caps finally receded, the climate became more temperate, and the herds of game less abundant. In this changing environment men learned to domesticate animals. They became herdsmen rather than hunters, they moved out of caves and into tents; they became nomads, continually searching for suitable grazing lands. This advance marks the beginning of what is called the Mesolithic (or Middle Stone) Age, and it is thought to have occurred about ten thousand years ago.

Then, perhaps two thousand years later (or at about the same time, according to some scholars), along the river banks of

Egypt, the Near East, and India, men learned to grow crops. This enabled them to settle permanently in villages, and the stage was set for the development of civilization and for the beginning of recorded history. From this time until about 3500 B.C., when copper came into use in Egypt (the date was much later in Europe), we are in the Neolithic (or New Stone) Age.

Ancient Egypt

When the snows melt each year in the mountains of Ethiopia, the Nile river swells and overflows its banks. Along these banks flourished the great civilization of ancient Egypt. The river banks were extremely fertile, but the floods could be destructive if not properly controlled. In response to the opportunity and challenge of the river, an intricately organized society evolved, able to control the annual floods by massive irrigation works. About 3500 B.C. absolute rule became vested in a Pharoah, whom the masses believed to be a divinity, and for almost three thousand years, through successive dynasties, and with only one interruption of any consequence, this remarkably efficient social organism maintained itself. The masses who had originally been mobilized for irrigation works, began, around 3000 B.C., to build the huge stone pyramids which served as tombs for the Pharoahs. Death, or rather preparation for life after death, played a dominant role in Egyptian culture, and our museums are full of their mummy cases and artifacts from their tombs.

In one sense it can be said that ancient Egypt was a civilization of the highest order. Certainly from an engineering point of view its accomplishments were extraordinary. It nurtured the growth of writing, mathematics and astronomy, painting and sculpture, fine weaving and other crafts. The Egyptians traded with all the known world of their age, collected taxes, conscripted armies, and maintained peace for long periods of time. Their religion, while pagan, was rich and imaginative. They sought honor and the good things of life. The Pharoahs, the priesthood, and, increasingly after 2500 B.C., the nobility enjoyed fine houses and luxurious furnishings. But the picture of nameless masses toiling like ants for the glory of the few is somehow repugnant to us. And a culture so preoccupied with death seems to have little relevance to our present concerns. Ancient Egypt remains, in more ways than one, a museum civilization.

Ancient Mesopotamia

In the Near East, in that part of the world which we today call Iraq, flow the Tigris and Euphrates rivers, swollen each year by the snows of Armenia. Like the Nile valley, the fertile land between these two rivers served as a "cradle of civilization." But where Egypt saw the rise of one cohesive culture, Mesopotamia (which means "the land between the rivers") spawned many different tribes, some of which grew into mighty, although relatively short-lived, empires.

About 3000 B.C. the Sumerians cultivated barley and dates, used silver ingots in trade, invented a cuneiform script, and built the royal tombs of Ur. About 2000 B.C. the Babylonians gained ascendency, creating the extraordinarily detailed legal Code of King Hammurabi and writing on clay tablets, many of which still remain as evidence of an active commercial society. Soon the Hittites came upon the scene, then Kassites, Hourrites, Phrygians, and Aramaeans—a swarming and counter-swarming of Semitic tribes. About 1500 B.C. the Hebrews appeared on the horizon of history escaping from Egyptian bondage and entering Palestine, their belief in a single God standing in stark contrast to the paganism all about them.

In the eighth and seventh centuries B.C. the warrior Assyrians swept irresistably across the land, establishing a much-feared empire with its capital at Nineveh. Then in 612 B.C. the Chaldeans seized control and proceeded to rebuild Babylon.

Their great emperor Nebuchadnezzar and one of his less worthy successors, Belshazzar, are well known to us from the Bible. In 538 B.C. the Persians, under King Cyrus, invaded from the east, out of present-day Iran, first overrunning Mesopotamia, and in 525 B.C. finally conquering Egypt.

With the establishment of the Persian Empire, the largest the world had known until this point, we find ourselves approaching a new era, more congenial to our modern temper than the fierce and turbulent times of Babylon and Ninevah. Those of us who remember any history at all should sense that with the mention of Persia we are approaching the age of mighty Persia's nemesis—Greece.

The age of Greece

About 2000 B.C. certain Indo-European tribes known as the Achaeans, the Ionians and the Dorians, later collectively known as Hellenes, started to descend through the Balkans onto the Greek peninsula. At the same time the so-called Aegeans were developing on Crete a thriving civilization which reached its height about 1600 B.C. and began spilling over onto the European and Asian shores of the Mediterranean. The Hellenes gradually infiltrated down through Greece and out onto the islands of the Aegean Sea. They overran the Aegeans, taking Crete about 1400 B.C. and conquering fabled Troy on the coast of Asia Minor about 1200 B.C.

The Greek peninsula is covered with mountains and indented with bays, effectively isolating one area from another. This precluded the growth of a large centrally governed empire and favored the development of several independent city-states. Athens, Sparta, Thebes, Corinth—the names of these city-states have come down through history covered with glory. These Hellenes, or Greeks, often argued amongst themselves, but they spoke a common language and developed a common culture; they considered all other peoples to be barbarians. The rocky terrain of Greece did not favor the growth of agriculture, but the Greeks became wealthy through mining, manufacture, and trade, and they established colonies throughout the Mediterranean. The political institutions of the city-states varied; they experimented with monarchies, dictatorships, oligarchies, and, in Athens, a democracy that served as a model and ideal for future generations.

In 492 B.C. Darius, the Persian king, launched an attack against Greece. This failed, but Darius tried again in 490, only to be defeated at the famous battle of Marathon. Ten years later Darius's son, Xerxes, once more moved against the Greeks, and in spite of a gallant stand by the Spartans at the pass of Thermopylae, the Persians prevailed and reached Athens, which they promptly burned. However, at Salamis, the Greek fleet, under Themistocles, won a stunning victory, and the Persians were thwarted again. After one more fruitless attack the following year, the Persians retired never to return.

In the years that followed, Greek civilization flourished in one of the most glorious episodes in all history. These were the years during which the Parthenon was built. Great works of sculpture and painting appeared in profusion. The dramas of Aeschylus, Sophocles, and Euripides were written and performed, as were the comedies of Aristophanes. Pericles represented political leadership at its finest. Socrates founded philosophy as we know it; Herodotus did the same for history. Protagoras taught geometry; Hippocrates, medicine.

This shining moment in history was not to last long. In 431 B.C. war broke out between Athens and Sparta. The Peloponnesian War, as it was called, lasted for twenty-seven years, and signalled the decline of Greek power. In 355 B.C. Philip of Macedon descended from the north upon the weakened and feuding Greek city-states, and by 338 all Greece was in his grasp.

Upon Philip's death two years later his son, Alexander, soon to be known as "the Great," succeeded to power. In 334 B.C. Alexander marched eastward, and in fourteen tumultuous years conquered most of the known civilized world. He made his way victoriously through Mesopotamia, Syria, and Egypt, through Persia and deep into India, before his rebellious army forced him to turn back. He died on the return journey, leaving behind him an heroic image for posterity, and a legacy of Greek culture throughout most of the lands he had overcome. The late blooming of Greek culture after Alexander is called *Hellenistic* to differentiate it from the earlier, or Hellenic, period. A great Hellenistic center arose in Alexandria, Egypt, where Euclid developed his theorems, and where talented astronomers, doctors, and scholars abounded.

But Alexander's short-lived empire soon disintegrated, the power of Greece was gone forever, and the center of world power began to shift westward—toward Rome.

The civilization of Greece represents a challenge and a rebuke to the engineer. For, although Hellenic engineering and craftsmanship were always adequate, and occasionally brilliant, the Greeks, at least from the time of Plato onward, considered technological activities unworthy of serious attention from the free citizen. They prized beauty and intellect, they worshipped excellence, and sought fame; but they scorned most practical pursuits. They admired strength and grace in athletics, but despised physical labor. They took delight in science, but in speculative science only; they spurned experimentation. Like engineers, they were unsentimental realists; but, unlike engineers, they were fatalistic and essentially pessimistic about the chances of improving things in the world. Like engineers they saw man as the measure of all things; but their vision of the good life contained no significant place for the engineer himself.

This prejudice of the Greeks has returned to haunt the engineer in more recent times. Where classical learning has defined the gentleman, engineering has been considered a vulgar calling.

Today, with technical education in the ascendance and classical learning in full retreat, there is no longer cause for us to feel resentful about this limitation in the Greek view of life. Rather should we join in the efforts of those who would see to it that the glory that was Greece is not soon forgotten.

The Roman Empire

Recent archeological finds have shown us that before 1000 B.C. a people known as the Etruscans had established an advanced civilization throughout most of northern Italy. About 750 B.C. the Etruscans seized from local Italian tribesmen a town called Rome, located on the Tiber River. About 500 B.C. the local inhabitants of Rome overthrew the ruling Etruscans, and the city once more became Italian, headquarters of an Italian tribe known as the Latins. By 275 B.C. these energetic and resourceful Latins were masters of most of Italy, and they soon came into conflict with Carthage, another great Mediterranean power which had been established by the Phoenicians on the northern coast of Africa. For more than a hundred years, starting in 264 B.C., the Romans fought intermittent wars against Carthage, finally emerging triumphant in spite of the exploits of the extraordinary Carthaginian general, Hannibal.

The Roman Republic, governed by a patrician Senate and two consuls, grew powerful and wealthy as it gradually established its rule throughout the Mediterranean. But greed and luxurious living took their toll; bickering and civil strife led to the cruel dictatorship of Sulla, and finally to the triumvirate of Pompey, Crassus, and Julius Caesar. We all know how Caesar led Roman armies of conquest through Gaul and into Britain, sending back reports of his prowess in the famous *Commentaries*, how he returned to Rome and drove Pompey from Italy, how he defeated Pompey's armies in Spain and Greece and pursued Pompey into Egypt, how he dallied there with Cleopatra, returned to Rome, and had himself declared dictator for life, and finally how, on the Ides of March, 44 B.C., he was assassinated by a group of senators led by Cassius and Brutus. The sequel to these events is equally well known. Marc Antony and Caesar's nephew, Octavian, avenged Caesar's death at Philippi, and then formed a new triumvirate with Lepidus. This led to new strife from which Octavian emerged triumphant after defeating Antony and Cleopatra in Egypt.

Octavian returned to Rome, adopted a new name, Augustus, and assumed the title of Imperator. The year was 27 B.C., the beginning of the Augustan Age. Under Augustus, and in the years to follow, the Roman Empire unified the world as it never has been unified since. Roman law was supreme, invincible Roman armies maintained the peace, Roman engineering and commerce flourished, and Roman citizenship, granted to peoples throughout the empire, insured a measure of security and justice. The concepts of law and order, duty and obedience to the state were established, never to be erased from the consciousness of Western man.

After Augustus, more than eighty emperors ruled in Rome. Some of them, such as Trajan, Hadrian, and Marcus Aurelius are known to have been noble and talented rulers; many, like Nero, were cruel and vicious; some were stupid, and some quite mad. However, in spite of corruption and confusion in Rome itself, the empire lived on.

Eventually barbarian tribes from the north and east began to press down upon Rome. Softened by generations of comfort, and weakened perhaps by disease, or depopulation, or the advent of Christianity, or by one or another of the numerous possible causes which historians are continually arguing about, Rome struggled vainly for survival. Sacked by the Visigoths in 410 A.D. and by the Vandals in 455, saved from the Huns by the fortunate death of the dreaded Attila, Rome finally fell to the Visigoths in 476.

In 330 A.D. the emperor Constantine had shifted his capital

east to the city of Byzantium, which he renamed Constantinople, and which today we know as Istanbul. By 395 the Empire was divided into two separate states with capitals at both Rome and Constantinople. After the Western Empire fell, the Eastern Empire, known as the Byzantine, survived for almost another one thousand years.

Constantine did one other thing which changed the course of history. In 311 A.D. he issued an edict assuring tolerance of Christianity throughout the Empire, and he eventually became a Christian himself, declaring Christianity the official religion of the Roman Empire. While Rome aged and fell, the Church was preparing itself to step forward as the next central force in world history.

If the Roman Empire is a testimonial to technology of which we engineers can be proud, its inadequacies must still give us pause. For all his accomplishments, there was a certain coarseness about the Roman which is not pleasant to behold. Noted classicist Edith Hamilton has put it in this way:

> Beauty was unimportant to him. Life in his eyes was a very serious and a very arduous business, and he had no time for what he would have thought of as a mere decoration of it . . . . There were imperative tasks to summon men for all that was in them. Painting, sculpture, such-like trifles, were to be left to what a Roman writer called "the hungry Greekling."[5]

More serious, perhaps, from the point of view of our modern predicament, the qualities of character which built the greatness of Rome were unequal to the challenge of saving her from eventual downfall. Again Miss Hamilton:

> The old virtues were completely inadequate for the new day. The abilities of the pioneer and the conqueror, which had made the empire, could not meet the conditions which resulted from their achievements. To overcome nature or nations calls for one set of qualities; to use the victory as a basis for a better state in human affairs calls for another. When men must turn

from extending their possessions to making wise use of them, audacity, self-reliance, endurance, are not enough. . . . It is worth our while to perceive that the final reason for Rome's defeat was the failure of mind and spirit to rise to a new and great opportunity, to meet the challenge of new and great events. Material development outstripped human development, the Dark Ages took possession of Europe, and classical antiquity ended.[6]

The Dark Ages

In the "Dark Ages" which followed the fall of Rome, barbarian tribes were on the move all over Europe—Goths, Vandals, Franks, Burgundians, Angles, and Saxons. Commerce was disrupted and literature and the arts all but vanished. The church stood as the only stable force, her pope in Rome, her bishops in every major city, and her monasteries and schools serving as the last sanctuaries of learning.

In 590 Pope Gregory the Great ascended to St. Peter's Chair in Rome and his efforts contributed in great measure to the building of a new Christian civilization throughout Europe. Even the heathen inhabitants of Britain were converted when Augustine crossed the Channel in 597.

Slowly the barbarian tribes began to evolve into Christian states. But it was not destined for these states to develop in peace. Out of the deserts of Arabia swept the Arabs (also called Saracens and Moors), who were inspired by the teachings of their prophet Mohammed. They became masters of Mecca in the year 630, rapidly conquered most of the Near East, then moved steadily west across northern Africa, entering Spain in 711. On they came, across the Pyrenees, and for a moment it appeared as if all Europe would fall before Islam. But Charles Martel led the Franks to a victory over the invaders at Tours in 732.

Europe was saved, but the shape and future course of Europe was far from decided. Charles Martel's grandson, Charles the

Great, or Charlemagne, became king of the Franks in 768, and set about expanding the borders of his kingdom. He succeeded in uniting what is now France, Belgium, Holland, western Germany, and northern Italy (although he could not drive the Moors from Spain), and on Christmas day in the year 800 he was declared Roman Emperor by the Pope. (There was still, you will recall, a so-called Roman Empire to the east with its capital in Constantinople, and from Charlemagne's time on there were two Empires once again.) Charlemagne did what he could to reestablish learning and the arts, but his rule provided only a flicker of light in what were essentially "dark" times.

After Charlemagne's death in 814, his empire was divided into three parts, and in succeeding years the Germanic part inherited the name of the Holy Roman Empire. The title of Holy Roman Emperor thereafter usually went to that Germanic king who was most in favor with the Pope, and he became the nominal overlord of such German dukedoms and Italian cities as could be persuaded to recognize him. It should be remembered that neither Germany nor Italy became single nations until about one hundred years ago.

No sooner had the Mohammedan advance been more or less stabilized than a new scourge descended upon Europe—the Vikings. From the north they came, these feared seagoing Norsemen, and all through the ninth and tenth centuries they attacked and pillaged. They eventually became converted to Christianity and settled in many of the places they had raided, notably in Normandy along the French coast. It was from Normandy that William the Conqueror, a descendant of the Norsemen, set out to conquer England in 1066. At Hastings he met and defeated Harold, and from that time forward England was governed by the Normans. William had no intention of giving up his holdings in Normandy, and so it happened that the early English kings ruled over part of France. This eventually led to one hundred years of war between the two nations.

The Middle Ages

At the time that William the Conqueror crossed the English Channel, Europe had reached a state of semiequilibrium with its Arab and Byzantine neighbors. Tribal migrations and invasions had come to an end. The renewal of civilization which we now call *the Middle Ages* was at hand.

Throughout Europe feudal society was beginning to emerge. Small self-sufficient communities grew up around fortified castles. Social organization was hierarchal: from the lord and his knights down to the lowliest serf, each man had his place, his role to play, and his obligations to other members of the community. Those on the lower rungs of the hierarchy grew the food and did the work; those above provided protection and did the fighting. Until large and stable nation-states could evolve again, feudalism served the needs of the people well enough.

There is something pleasing about the orderliness of the medieval world as we look back upon it from our fluid ever-changing society. Not only did each man have his assigned place, but he was confident that this place was sanctioned by God and His Church, as was indeed the entire scheme of things. Everyone knew how he was expected to behave. For the upper classes the code of chivalry served as a guide, much violated in practice no doubt, but still an ideal which shines brightly through the ages. Later centuries were to look back patronizingly on the "Middle Ages," as if they were an inferior interlude between antiquity and the rediscovery of antiquity. And it is true that these times were filled with cruelty, pain, and superstition. Freedom of action was impossible and freedom of inquiry almost equally so. But modern men, disenchanted with the fruits of progress and materialism, are experiencing a nostalgic rebirth of appreciation for this vanished world.

We engineers are committed to change and to the future. Nevertheless the magnificent cathedrals of medieval Europe

speak to us hauntingly of the ideals of universal order, selfless-
ness, and faith.

The Crusades

In the second half of the eleventh century a new and threaten-
ing force arose in the east. The Turks descended from Central
Asia and wrested control of most of the Moslem world from the
Arabs. They abused Christian pilgrims in Palestine and fright-
ened the Byzantine Empire, which called to Rome for help.
Western Christendom's answer was the Crusades. For more than
one hundred years, starting in 1095, successive crusades journeyed east to the Holy Land. There were initial successes, and
Latin Crusading States were established, lasting in Jerusalem
until 1187 and in Tripoli until 1289. But the Crusades were
tarnished by men's baser instincts and ultimately disintegrated
into little more than piratical raids. The Eastern Empire lived
to regret its call for assistance. The westerners plundered as they
went, actually sacking Constantinople itself in 1203. In the end
the Turks regained all they had lost, and eventually toppled
Byzantium, capturing Constantinople in 1453.

A by-product of the Crusades, or perhaps one of its causes,
was the growth of trade between West and East. At the cross-
roads of this commercial activity was Venice, which grew into a
wealthy and powerful maritime republic. Marco Polo, who near
the end of the thirteenth century traveled to the court of the
Mongol Khans in China, was a Venetian merchant.

The growth of nations
in the Middle Ages

From the eleventh to the fifteenth centuries European feudal
communities gradually combined forces, and the outlines of
nations began to emerge. The kings only had such power as
the nobles could be persuaded to grant (witness the Magna

Carta which the English nobles forced King John to sign in 1215), but this power grew steadily. Within the new nations civil strife was unceasing, and between the nations warfare was a way of life. From 1337 to 1453 England and France fought almost continually in what we now call the Hundred Years' War. England won glorious victories at Crécy, Poitiers, and Agincourt, but in the end the French, with Joan of Arc to lead them, expelled the English from the continent. Within two years the English were at each other's throats as the houses of Lancaster and York battled for supremacy in the Wars of the Roses; and France was soon embroiled in her own war with Burgundy. Out of this bloodshed the nationhood of England and France was forged. In Spain the Christian kingdoms of Castile and Aragon steadily forced the Moors southward, and in 1492 Ferdinand and Isabella completed the job of uniting the nation and of driving out the "infidels" completely.

As national identities took shape the feudal way of life began to dissolve. (The introduction of cannon, it will be recalled, made castles obsolete.) Cities began to grow in size and in importance. In the cities guilds of skilled craftsmen arose which controlled the education and work habits of their members, established prices and the quality of goods, and jealously guarded the good name and power of their brotherhood. This is one more example of the medieval passion for order, one which strikes a responsive chord in today's engineer. After all, these guilds were the precursors of our own professional societies.

The Renaissance

If a year is to be selected for the end of the Middle Ages and the beginning of the Renaissance (the "rebirth"), 1453 will serve as well as any other. This was the year, as we have noted, in which the Turks captured Constantinople, an event which had two crucial effects. First, it drove many of the scholars and scientists of the Byzantine Empire west to Italy, bringing with them the remaining cultural heritage of Greece and Rome. Second, it effectively closed the trade routes between Europe and the East, and started men thinking about reaching the Orient via the great ocean which lay to the west.

Italy was fertile soil for the rebirth of ancient thought and for the flowering of the "new learning." The city-states—Florence, Rome, Bologna, Padua, Venice, Perugia, Milan—although they bickered continuously among themselves, had grown prosperous from the Mediterranean trade of which they were the hub. The Italians had always been skilled merchants, but, even more important, they became accomplished bankers. Italian wealth resulted in support for the arts and a new independence of thought. Scholars began to think less about the nature of God, and more about man; they called themselves "humanists." The influx of learned men from Byzantium reinforced currents which were already flowing.

The Italian Renaissance reached its height in Florence from 1469 to 1492 under the rule of Lorenzo de Medici, and in Rome from 1513 to 1521 under Lorenzo's son, Pope Leo X. In the fine arts this is the richest period in all history. Michelangelo and Leonardo da Vinci, Botticelli, Raphael, and Titian—these are a few of the names that contributed to the glory of the Italian Renaissance.

In the years that followed, this artistic and intellectual revolution moved throughout Europe and finally reached a new apex in Elizabethan England at the end of the sixteenth century. (Let us not forget the role played in this diffusion by the discovery of printing.)

The Age of Exploration

Meanwhile, along the Atlantic shore, the great explorations were under way. The need for new trade routes was crucial. Technologically the conquest of the oceans was now possible and there were a number of valiant men ready to undertake this conquest. First the Portugese sailed south along the coast of Africa: in 1486 Bartholomew Diaz rounded the Cape of Good Hope; in 1498 Vasco da Gama reached India, establishing a rich commerce which served Portugal well for a century. From Spain the voyagers headed west into the ocean—Columbus to America in 1492, Magellan to circumvent the world in 1520, Cortez to conquer Mexico in 1525, and Pizarro to conquer Peru in 1533. Through Spain the new world's gold and silver flowed copiously into Europe, making Spain rich and providing much-needed currency for expansion of trade. Through Portugal came spices and other goods from the Orient.

Wealth is readily converted into power, and during the sixteenth century Spain became the leading nation in Europe. At one time Charles V, grandson of Ferdinand and Isabella, ruled Spain, Naples, Sicily, Flanders, the Netherlands, and—because he also had a Hapsburg grandfather—Austria. He was proclaimed emperor of the Holy Roman Empire in 1535. His son, Philip II, annexed Portugal to the Spanish crown. But Philip met his match in Elizabeth of England, whose ships defeated the Spanish armada in 1588. Also by this time the Netherlands, having grown rich as a clearinghouse for ocean trade, had revolted and thrown off the Spanish yoke. As the world entered the seventeenth century, Spain had passed the peak of her glory.

The Reformation

In the intellectual and political ferment of these years the Church of Rome did not escape untouched. For a long time there had been growing disenchantment with the conduct of the popes and their clergy. In 1517 a German monk named Martin Luther nailed on the door of the Wittenberg cathedral his Ninety-five Theses, points on which he disagreed with the declared dogma of the Church. Primarily he objected to the role that the Church played as intermediary between men and God; he spoke out on behalf of the individual conscience. Summoned before Emperor Charles V in 1521 at a church meeting known as the Diet of Worms, Luther refused to recant. This marked the beginning of what is called the *Reformation,* the birth of Protestantism. Soon John Calvin was preaching in Geneva, and throughout northern Europe the new religion made headway. Protestantism had a genuine religious appeal, but this was far from being the only reason for its success. Men were disgusted with decadence in Rome, resentful of the taxes that Rome demanded, and jealous of the Church's wealth. In England Henry VIII was happy to use the excuse of his divorce from Catherine of Aragon to break with Rome and to confiscate the Church's extensive land holdings. In the end most of the Germanic states, Holland, the Scandinavian lands, and England became Protestant. Spain, Austria, the Italian states, and most of France remained Catholic.

The Church fought back. From 1545 until 1563 Catholic leaders met at the Council of Trent. Many reforms were made, the beliefs of the Church were restated, and a Counter-Reformation was planned. The dreaded Spanish Inquisition followed. Soon all of Europe was plunged in bloody wars pitting Catholics against Protestants. The bloodiest of all was the Thirty Years' War, which was waged from 1618 to 1648, mostly within the borders of Germany, then still known as the Holy Roman Empire. France, under Louis XIII and Cardinal Richelieu, seized the opportunity to enter this war for her own political benefit, even though it meant attacking fellow Catholics in Spain and Germany. France prevailed. An already weakened Spain and a feeble Holy Roman Empire were no match for France and her Protestant allies.

The War was ended by the Treaty of Westphalia, which established France as the major European power, ratified the independence of Protestant Holland and Switzerland, and confirmed the right of each state in the Holy Roman Empire to establish its own religion.

The end of the Renaissance

Let us look for a moment at Europe just after the Treaty of Westphalia in 1648, almost two hundred years after the date that we chose to mark the transition from the Middle Ages to the Renaissance. The intellectual, artistic, and cultural renaissance had run its course from Italy through the continent to England. The English Renaissance, which we call the Elizabethan Age, was over. Elizabeth I, who gave the age its name, died in 1603, and William Shakespeare, its brightest star, in 1616. Elizabeth's successors, the Stuarts, had just been deposed by Oliver Cromwell and his Puritans. Soon Charles I was to be beheaded. This period marked the beginning of solemn days in England.

The age of the great explorations was also over, and an age of colonization had begun. Walter Raleigh's expedition to Virginia took place in 1583; the Virginia Company was founded in 1606; the Pilgrims founded New Plymouth in 1620.

The religious wars were over. The Reformation and the Counter-Reformation were things of the past.

Truly we can say that the Renaissance had ended. Yet the new sense of the worth of the individual, the new attitude of inquisitiveness, the new rebellion against authority—these forces had lost none of their vitality. On the contrary, joined with the rising tide of scientific discovery which was just beginning to be felt, the forces unleashed by the Renaissance were to sweep through the civilized world again and again in the years ahead.

England and France after 1660 —a study in contrast

Let us take up our story again twelve years later. In 1660 two new monarchs took the center of the European stage. In

England, with Cromwell dead, the Stuarts were recalled, and
Charles II became king. The merry, wicked days of the Restoration were at hand. Louis XIV was crowned in France. The
magnificent reign of the Sun King began. By considering what
happened to these two nations in the years after 1660, we can
capture the mainstream of modern history in capsule form.

In England the Stuarts did not last long. James II was deposed in a bloodless revolution in 1688. William of Orange and
Mary were invited to take the English throne, but not before
they signed an agreement known as the Bill of Rights. From
that time forward the power of the English monarchy was increasingly curbed, and government by the prime minister and
Parliament took its place. English political history has not by
any means been placid during the past three hundred years.
There have been riots and uproars aplenty. But the crucial
transition from rule by monarchy to rule by Parliament was
made relatively smoothly. True representative government followed slowly but inevitably as popular suffrage was demanded
and won.

How different was the case in France. Louis XIV ruled supreme from 1660 to his death in 1715. The reign of his son,
Louis XV, lasted until 1774. This was truly, as it has been
called, "the century of France." French commerce prospered,
French armies prevailed, and French culture, emanating from
the splendor that was Versailles, dazzled the world. Modern
engineering, as we have previously mentioned, was born in
France at this time.

But absolute monarchy came to mean absolute misery for the
masses. In 1789 the French Revolution, the "deluge" which
Louis XV had predicted, engulfed the hapless nation. Louis XVI
paid with his head, as did thousands more during the Reign of
Terror. The Revolution started under the direction of the middle class. It soon was taken over by the mob. Within ten years
it was in the hands of the military.

The collapse of the revolution and the pressure of a hostile

Europe placed France in the hands of Napoleon Bonaparte, who streaked like a meteor across the skies of history. First Consul in 1799, emperor by 1804, Napoleon was the lord of all Europe in 1812; he was defeated by England's Duke of Wellington at Waterloo in 1815.

France reverted to a monarchy, changed to a "citizen king," Louis Philippe, after the Revolution of 1830, traded him in for President Louis Napoleon after the Revolution of 1848, then quickly allowed the new president to become Emperor Napoleon III. Napoleon III fell from power after losing a war to Prussia in 1870, and democracy of a sort finally came to France.

Monarchy, which had filled a genuine need in the Middle Ages, helping to forge nation-states and serving to protect the masses from high-handed lords, ended its useful life at the threshold of modern times. Either it evolved into constitutional monarchy, or became absolute tyranny destined for violent over-throw. In England, and later in the United States of America, political institutions were developed which were resilient enough to absorb the thrusts of power from one group after an-other without tearing apart the social fabric. In France, as in much of the world (notably in this century, Russia), the "old guard" held on to unworkable institutions until revolution be-came inevitable.

Yet institutions themselves do not provide a final answer. The societies which have made the most successful transition into modern times seem to be possessed of a certain common sense, a pragmatic restraint. The "establishment" yields just as much as it must to avoid losing all; the "outs" grasp just as much as they can without toppling authority and bringing on anarchy.

The Age of Reason

Whence came this impulse to reorganize society, to establish the "rights" of all men instead of the privileges of the few? No doubt, as the established hierarchy ceased to serve their needs, men instinctively and restlessly cast about for ways to better their lot. But whence came the *ideas* which prompted them to action and around which they could rally? The answer is that these ideas were born in that cultural period of western civilization which has come to be called the Age of Reason.

As we have noted in the previous chapter, the seventeenth century saw the beginnings of modern science. Men began to learn that by studying nature experimentally and using their minds logically, they could arrive at "truths." These truths could be tested and reconfirmed. They seemed to be superior in quality to the earlier truths of tradition, superstition, and scripture. This discovery came to men of intellect as a revelation. They became enamored of *reason*.

From science this idea spread rapidly to philosophy (Descartes said, "I reason, therefore I exist."), and then to political philosophy. Men came to believe—how naïvely we now know— that the human mind must be naturally rational and that the ills of mankind are therefore attributable to ignorance and bad institutions. All that men had to do, it followed, was to discover, and then live by, the true laws of human and social behavior which somehow "existed" in nature. Accordingly, a lot of attention was paid to man in his primitive state, and a lot of nonsense was written about the "noble savage." Religion was not abandoned entirely, for morality without God did not seem to make sense. But God was thought of as the creator of a wonderful universe-machine which now ran on without His further interference—a religious view known as Deism. Rational men, it was concluded, could learn to live happily within the pattern of a not unfriendly universe. Out of such thinking developed the concept of the "natural rights" of man.

During the eighteenth century men began to talk of their age as a time of *enlightenment*. This term first was used in France, where Voltaire, Rousseau, and the *philosophes* were propounding the ideas that led inevitably to the French Revolution. Across the Channel, reason ruled supreme in the London of Samuel Johnson and Alexander Pope. Across the ocean such apostles of reason as Thomas Jefferson shaped the foundations of our American republic.

The intellectuals of the Enlightenment were not radicals, as we know the term. They were well-meaning and humanistic, but still undeniably aristocratic in outlook. In the words of one cultural historian, the age was "a kind of honeymoon of the intellectual with the masses."[7]

The art and literature of the time, as we shall see in later chapters, was marked by a restraint and orderliness which characterizes it as "classical." A later age was to complain that it was cold and formalistic. Its defenders have claimed it was distinguished by clarity, precision, wit, brilliance, incisiveness, and good sense.

The Romantic revolution —The downfall of reason

As the eighteenth century drew to a close, reason was toppled from her throne. She had reigned for almost a century and a half. The revolutionaries who toppled her were the "romantics"—such men as Shelley, Byron and Keats, Goethe and Wordsworth. The heart once more took precedence over the head. Passion and sentiment ruled supreme. Mystery and medievalism returned to favor. The man of feeling replaced the man of reason as an ideal.

Along with a revolution in artistic taste the nineteenth century witnessed a growing intellectual disenchantment with the concept of reason. This disenchantment was partly the result of the natural swing of the cultural pendulum away from one view of man which had prevailed for more than a century; it was partly the result of the turbulence resulting from the French

Revolution and the restless stirring of the masses throughout Europe; it was partly a result of uneasiness accompanying the start of the Industrial Revolution. Ultimately, however, disenchantment was inevitable. Men simply refused to behave reasonably. Freud was some day to show the world a few of the reasons why.

In the twentieth century the downfall of reason has been succeeded by its disparagement. In a world gone mad, who can believe in the rational processes of the human mind? Besides, the growth of the social sciences has discredited many of the prized beliefs of the Age of Reason. Anthropology has shown that the "noble savage" is a myth. Psychology has discovered the powerful force of the unconscious. Sociology, economics, and political science are still trying to come to grips with the phenomenon of mob behavior. Not only the social sciences but science itself has contributed to the downfall of reason. In the mid-nineteenth century Darwin demonstrated that man is not discontinuous from the animal kingdom, but has grown directly out of an ancient mixture of instinct and brute behavior. Modern physics, with its rejection of Newtonian determinism, has destroyed the very foundations of clarity and certainty on which the Enlightenment rested. (We shall have more to say about this in Chapter 6.)

Yet to the engineer, the concept of reason is not something to be surrendered hastily and without a battle. "Our disappointments are real," admits Charles Frankel in *The Case for Modern Man*. "But they are real because our powers are great and our expectations legitimately high." The revival of our hopes, he points out, "does not depend on initially disparaging the technical powers and the secular intelligence which must be our main instruments in dealing with our problems."[8]

However limited and naïve its outlook, the Age of Reason remains, for the engineer in particular, a golden age worthy of fond remembrance. Indeed, as one historian of science has written, "we can pardon, and even envy, that age for its temporary self-satisfaction."[9]

Self-satisfaction is something that we of the twentieth century can ill afford. Even less can we afford to abandon altogether our faith in rationality.

The modern era

The Age of Reason and the Romantic Revolution that followed it have carried us into the middle of the nineteenth century. We last spoke of France and England in 1870, with France finally achieving democracy after the fall of Napoleon III and England making steady advances under her constitutional monarchy. (From 1837 to 1901 England prospered under the rule of Queen Victoria.)

There is much more to be told about the nineteenth century. Wars between the European powers were numerous and complex; Africa and Australia were explored; overseas empires were established and extended. The flame of freedom continued to burn brightly, fanned by the fervor of Romanticism. After heroic struggles, Italy and Germany established their nationhood; Latin America freed itself from Spain; Greece and other Balkan nations threw off the Turkish yoke. Russia and Japan grew into major powers. The Industrial Revolution changed ways of living for much of the world. Grudgingly, laws were passed to improve the lot of the working classes; but the dream of equality of opportunity was far from being realized. In 1848 Marx and Engels issued the *Communist Manifesto*.

The United States expanded its frontiers to the west, fought a tragic civil war, and then, nourished by successive immigrations from Europe, embarked on an unparalleled growth in wealth and power. After 1870 there were years of relative stability and optimism. But the brief period of tranquility was shattered by the world war of 1914.

All of this is most interesting, but for our present purpose perhaps less worthy of attention than the earlier historical periods previously considered. We are, after all, modern men, more or less familiar with the problems, achievements, and dis-illusionments of the modern era. Most of us also have a pretty sound feeling for the history and traditions of our own young nation. The danger lies in our forgetting or ignoring those earlier ages which shaped the western civilization to which we are heirs.

For the moment this danger has been partially overcome. We have refreshed our memories and stand, amazed, before the awesome tapestry of the past.

Recommended reading

Thomas Carlyle said that "the history of the world is but the biography of great men." As a theory of history this is debatable. But as an introduction to the history of an age I know of nothing that can equal a good biography. Historical facts have a way of slipping through the mind. But a striking personality is not readily forgotten; and a good biographer so cloaks his subject in the times in which he lived that in remembering the man we remember the era. The following (in historical order) are just a few of the dozens of excellent biographies available: Paul Murray Kendall, *Richard the Third* (Anchor Books A455); Samuel Eliot Morison, *Christopher Columbus, Mariner* (Mentor Books MP439); Garrett Mattingly, *Catherine of Aragon* (Vintage Books V92); Zoë Oldenbourg, *Catherine the Great* (Bantam Books N3134); Carl Van Doren, *Benjamin Franklin* (Compass Books C163); Catherine Drinker Bowen, *John Adams and the American Revolution* (Universal Library 24-UL); André Maurois, *Disraeli* (Modern Library, 1942); Winston S. Churchill, *My Early Life: A Roving Commission* (Scribner SL25); Robert E. Sherwood, *Roosevelt and Hopkins* (Universal Library 79-UL).

Also worthy of mention are Harold Lamb's popular biographies: *Charlemagne, Cyrus the Great, Ghengis Khan, Hannibal* and *Theodora and the Emperor* (all Bantam Books). Notable multivolume American biographies of our time are Douglas Southall Freeman's *Robert E. Lee* (Scribner, 1934–1935) and *George Washington* (Scribner, 1948) and Carl Sandburg's *Abraham Lincoln* (Dell 0008).

Another enjoyable approach to history is through the historical novel. A few good ones: Mika Waltari, *The Egyptian* (Pocket Books 75022); Mary Renault, *The King Must Die* (Vintage Books V297); Robert Graves, *Hercules, My Shipmate* (Pyramid Books S-1346); Thornton Wilder, *The Ides of March* (Universal Library 13-UL); Marguerite Yourcenar, *Memoirs of Hadrian* (Noonday Press H258); Frans G. Bengtsson, *The Long Ships*—about the Vikings (Signet Books T2491); Zoë Oldenbourg, *Destiny of Fire*—the Crusades (Ballantine Books U7031); Hope Muntz, *The Golden Warrior*—the battle of Hastings (Scribner SL91); Kenneth Roberts, *Northwest Passage*—prerevolutionary America (Crest Books M610).

Then there are the "popular" writers of history. Novelist Thomas B. Costain has written a swashbuckling four-volume *History of the Plantagenets* (Popular Library W1144-48-51-33). *The Armada* by Garrett Mattingly (Sentry Editions 17) is high adventure and wonderful history. Winston Churchill's *A History of the English-Speaking Peoples* (Bantam Books CK103) and *The Second World War* (Bantam Books TK100) are brilliant works of individualistic historical literature. Alan Moorehead, in my opinion the most enjoyably readable nonfiction writer of our time, has written the splendid *The Blue Nile* (Dell 0636), *The White Nile* (Dell 9516), *Cooper's Creek*—about the exploration of Australia (Dell 1463), *The Fatal Impact* (Harper & Row, 1966)—about the opening up of the Pacific, *Gallipoli* (Perennial Library P53), and *The Russian Revolution* (Perennial Library P45).

We come, at last, to the professional historians. A fine introduction to the field for those interested in the nature of history itself is Fritz Stern (ed.), *The Varieties of History* (Meridian Books M37), an anthology of essays about their craft written by noted historians from Voltaire to the present. Charles Frankel, *The Case for Modern Man* (Beacon Books BP74), is a study of several contemporary philosophies of history by a staunch defender of the "liberal" belief in progress.

For the reader who "wants the facts" there are quite a few one-volume histories of the world available, among them: L. J. Cheney, *A History of the Western World* (Mentor Books MD274); Stewart C. Easton, *A Brief History of the Western World* (Barnes & Noble No. 284); René Sédillot, *The History of the World in 240 Pages* (Mentor Books MP411). A brief, lucid, and attractive introductory work is the multivolume *Great Ages of Man* (Time-Life Books). A monumental work, very appealing to the average reader because of its brisk and friendly style, is Will Durant's *The Story of Civilization* (Simon and Schuster). The ten volumes that this work comprises are an education in themselves. They are recommended highly yet hesitantly because of their great length. Arnold J. Toynbee, *A Study of History* (Galaxy Books 74 through 85) is a classic of our age, but even in a two-volume abridgement (Dell 8374LE) it is a formidable work. Its sweeping theories are debatable, and it is recommended only for those with time and patience to spare. A classic of earlier times still deserving of being included in any list of historical reading: Edward Gibbon, *The Decline and Fall of the Roman Empire*, available in many editions and abridgements.

A selection of solid works dealing with individual periods or nations: V. Gordon Childe, *What Happened In History*—prehistory and ancient times (Penguin Books A108); John Bagnell Bury, *History of Greece* (Modern Library Giants G35); Donald R. Dudley, *The Civilization of Rome* (Mentor Books MT472);

Henri Pirenne, *Economic and Social History of Medieval Europe* (Harvest Books HB14); Henry S. Lucas, *The Renaissance and the Reformation* (Harper & Row, 1960); Warren H. Lewis, *The Splendid Century*—the seventeenth century (Anchor Books A122); Georges Lefebvre, *The Coming of the French Revolution* (Vintage Books V43); George M. Trevelyan, *Shortened History of England* (Penguin Books A443); William Miller, *New History of the United States* (Dell 6328).

Three very skilled and deservedly popular historians of our day are: Bruce Catton, *Mr. Lincoln's Army* (Pocket Books 75034), *A Stillness at Appomattox* (Pocket Books 75015), and other works on the American Civil War; Arthur M. Schlesinger, Jr., *The Age of Jackson* (Little, Brown LB18) or the abridged version (Mentor Books MD145) and *The Age of Roosevelt* (Sentry Editions 36 and 39); Barbara W. Tuchman, *The Guns of August* (Dell 3333) and *The Proud Tower*—dealing with the period prior to World War I (Macmillan, 1965). For the history of this century, see two illuminating books by George F. Kennan: *American Diplomacy 1900–1950* (Mentor Books MP360) and *Russia and the West Under Lenin and Stalin* (Mentor Books MQ459).

And, finally, the aristocrats of the historical fraternity, the "cultural" historians, the scholars who do not deal in dates and "events" but rather seek to define the underlying moods and meanings of civilizations. A few of the classics in this field: Edith Hamilton, *The Greek Way* (W. W. Norton N230) and *The Roman Way* (W. W. Norton N232); J. Huizinga, *The Waning of the Middle Ages* (Anchor Books A42); Basil Willey *The Seventeenth Century Background* (Anchor Books A19); Jacques Barzun, *Classic, Romantic and Modern* (Anchor Books A255) and *Darwin, Marx, Wagner* (Anchor Books A127).

CHAPTER FOUR

The Bridge
to Literature:
The Engineer
as a Protagonist
in Fiction

Men have been telling stories for as long as they have had words with which to speak. Tales are told and retold mainly for the interest, insight, and pleasure they afford. But a society's myths, legends, and popular tales also serve as a means of transmitting moral instruction and philosophical opinion. The storyteller says to his audience, in effect, "Listen to the saga of my hero; he is a great man who deserves our admiration, and we should all try to behave as nobly as he." Or else, "Listen to the doings of this scoundrel; he is a disgrace to us all." Or perhaps, "Listen to what befell this ordinary man; it might happen to us unless we mend our ways; or it might happen to us no matter what we do, since that is the way of the world."

The heroes and villains of literature tell us much about values and mores as they have changed through the ages. Homer's Achilles is proud, strong, independent, and egotistical; Virgil's Aeneas is devoted to the service of the state. Defoe's Robinson Crusoe is a resourceful representative of the middle class, while the real heroes of Tolstoy's *War and Peace* are the passive and fatalistic peasants. In the novels of D. H. Lawrence fulfillment is found in sex; in Hemingway the supreme virtue is courage. Other authors see salvation in beauty, martyrdom, amusement, fame, love—the list is as long and diverse as is the range of human experience. The variety is dazzling, but each author's vision serves to illuminate some facet of the civilization from which he springs.

All types of literature serve to entertain, enlighten, and inspire us, regardless of our professions. But, as engineers, should we not be particularly interested in seeing where our own profession appears in the literature of our age? How are we engineers depicted by our literary contemporaries? What image do we project? As we see ourselves suddenly reflected in the mirror of fiction, we cannot help but be drawn—like Alice through the looking glass—into the strange and wondrous world of literature.

An almost forgotten tradition

When James A. Michener's novel, *Caravans,* was published in 1963, and rose rapidly to the upper regions of the best-seller list, it marked the rebirth of an almost forgotten literary tradition—the popular novel with a dashing engineer hero.

Mr. Michener had his heroine, a disillusioned and confused college girl, run off to Afghanistan with a native civil engineer, a builder of dams. This engineer, Nazrullah by name, is "an attractive fellow," "wiry," and endowed with "a mercurial brilliance in both gesture and speech." His imagination is "inflamed," and he rushes about "with boundless vitality," exclaiming "with infectious enthusiasm." "I want to stir the earth," he cries out, "fundamentally . . . , in the bowels."

In short, he is the spiritual son of Warren Neale, the engineer hero of Zane Grey's *The U. P. Trail* who was "wild for adventure, keen for achievement, eager, ardent, bronze-faced, and keen-eyed," a man who "had been seized by the spirit of some great thing to be." And both Nazrullah and Neale are descendants of the stalwart Findlayson, tamer of the Ganges, hero of Rudyard Kipling's story, *The Bridge-Builders*.

Kipling, indeed, must be regarded as the one who originated this genre, and he did almost as much in his day toward improving the image of the engineer as he did toward that of the British tommy. Kipling was convinced that as the nineteenth century came to a close, a new era was dawning that would see poverty and superstition swept from the face of the earth. And in his famous story he depicted the engineer as the symbol of this new age of greatness.

The scene is set in India, where a bridge across the Ganges River is nearing completion. It is for the most part the work of one man, a British civil engineer by the name of Findlayson, who has designed the bridge and supervised its construction through three arduous years.

> Findlayson, C. E., turned on his trolley and looked over the face of the country that he had changed for seven miles around. Looked back on the humming village of five thousand workmen; upstream and down, along the vista of spurs and sand; across the river to the far piers, lessening in the haze; overhead to the guard towers—and only he knew how strong those were

—and with a sigh of contentment saw that his work was good . . . .

But torrential rains bring a flood along the Ganges, and the great work is threatened. At the height of the storm, in a scene of wild fantasy, the fabled gods of India appear, bewailing the fact that they have been unable to destroy the creation of the Western intruders. They fear that once the people of India see that their gods are powerless to wreak vengeance on the bridge builders, they will begin to deny their ancient beliefs and place their faith in modern technology. Indeed, victory does go to the bridge builders as, after their intrepid protective efforts, the bridge survives the torrent.

Intelligent, dedicated, and tenacious, the engineer, to Kipling, is the most admirable of men, carrying to the far corners of the earth the banner of the most worthy of civilizations.

What was Troy to this?

Kipling's compatriot, Robert Louis Stevenson, was equally enthusiastic about the potentialities of engineering, not only as a force for the improvement of society, but also as a subject for literature. Traveling through the western United States in the 1870s, he came upon the transcontinental railroad then under construction, and was entranced. "If it be romance," he wrote, "if it be contrast, if it be heroism we require, what was Troy to this?"[1]

Stevenson never wrote the great epic of railroad construction he had envisioned, but there were many others to take up his challenge. The titles of their novels, most of them dating from the first twenty-five years of this century, have a pulse-quickening ring even to our sophisticated ears. *The Iron Trail, End of Steel, The Trail of the Lonesome Pine, Whispering Smith, The Fight on the Standing Stone, The Fire Bringers, Empire Build-*

ers—all of these are naïve and poorly written yet engaging in their ardent admiration for the vitality, ability, and courage of men who could span a continent with steel rails.

One of the most popular of all was *The Winning of Barbara Worth* by Harold Bell Wright, published in 1911. One passage in this book pretty well sums up the way engineers were regarded by the writers in this school:

> It was the last night out. Supper was over and the men, with their pipes and cigarettes, settled themselves in various careless attitudes of repose after the long day. . . . All were strong, clean-cut, vigorous specimens of intelligent, healthy manhood, for in all the professions, not excepting the army and navy, there can be found no finer body of men than our civil engineers.

Who today writes in this vein about the engineer? Very few authors, indeed. Occasionally a female novelist will have her heroine follow a romantic engineer to some exotic frontier. Anya Seton's *Foxfire* comes to mind, as well as Han Suyin's *The Mountain Is Young*, Vivien R. Bretherton's *The Rock and the Wind*, and Pamela Hinkson's *Golden Rose*. Every so often an engineer shows up in an adventure tale, such as Eric Ambler's *State of Siege*, Elleston Trevor's *The Flight of the Phoenix*, or Pierre Boulle's *The Bridge Over the River Kwai*. But the dashing, creative, constructive engineer of a few decades ago seems to have all but vanished from the literary scene.

Where the engineer does appear at all, we are apt to find him used by the novelist as a symbol of all that seems to have gone wrong with the world in this age of technological splendor and spiritual decay.

Modern man at his worst

"I became an engineer." With these words John Hersey begins his novel, *A Single Pebble*, an incisively critical examination of engineering viewed against an ancient and forbidding backdrop.

> I found my way into hydraulics, and not many years along, while still a youthful dam surveyor, I was chosen by the big contracting firm for which I worked to go to China and study the river, called by the Chinese, "The Great," the Yangtze, to see whether it would make sense for my company to try to sell the Chinese government a vast power project in the river's famous gorges.
>
> This was half my life ago, in the century's and my early twenties; the century and I were both young and sure of ourselves then.

Young and sure of himself, Hersey's hero embarks on an old junk for his trip up the Yangtze. But as the long and slow voyage unfolds his cockiness begins to wane. First the primeval wildness of the landscape makes him uneasy.

> We were all hopeless insects in this setting. My career, engineering, seemed only nonsense here. Nothing—absolutely nothing—could be done by man's puny will for this harsh valley littered with gigantic rocks.

Next he is disconcerted by the lovely poetry recited by the captain's wife, and he reacts petulantly.

> I protested to myself that my knowledge was useful; I could help to assuage poverty; my knowledge might help one day to make the electric light bulbs cast their healing, teaching glow into every mat shed clinging to these poverty-washed river banks. What was idle verse to that?

Finally the awesome weight of centuries-old tradition bears down upon him as he comes to realize that the river folk despise him and his plans to change their dangerous and arduous way of life.

> How could I, in the momentary years of my youth, have a part in persuading these people to tolerate the building of a

great modern dam that would take the waters of Tibet and Inner China with their age-old furies, on its back, there to grow lax and benign? How could I span a gap of a thousand years— a millenium in a day? These people on the junk could be said to be living in the era between Charlemagne and William the Conqueror, in the time of serfs and villeins, before the Crusades, before Western printing and gunpowder, long before Chaucer and Giotto and Thomas Aquinas and Dante. And they were satisfied (or so I thought) to exist in Dark Ages, while I lived in a time of enlightenment and was not satisfied.

Brash and callow is modern man, implies Hersey. And the engineer exemplifies modern man at his worst, impudent and insensitive. Our great technological achievements have resulted in a society filled with anxiety and dissatisfaction. Is it not possible that we have taken a wrong turn somewhere?

The inadequacy of our affluent but discontented society is also the theme of an impassioned novel by Norwegian novelist Johan Bojer entitled *The Great Hunger*. The protagonist, Peer Holm, rises from impoverished beginnings to become a successful engineer with great works to his credit on several continents. But success and accomplishment bring him only fleeting gratification. He expresses his disillusionment to a friend who has sensed his melancholy mood.

> "You seem to despise your own trade—as engineer?"
> "Yes," said Peer.
> "And why?"
> "Why, I feel the lack of some touch of beauty in our ceaseless craving to create something new, something new, always something new. More gold, more speed, more food . . . ."

The quest for ever-increasing speeds in transportation is particularly distressing to Peer.

> Are the children of the earth grown so homeless? Do they fear to take a moment's rest? Do they dread to look inward and see their own emptiness? Are they longing for something they have lost—some hymn, some harmony, some God?

The longer he lives, the more the sight of humanity fervently striving for material progress appears to him to be senseless and misdirected.

> The great evolutionary stream, with its wonders of steel and miracles of science, goes marching on victoriously, I grant you, changing the face of the world, hurrying its pulse to a more and more feverish beat. But what good will it do the peasant to be able to fly through the air on his wheelbarrow while no temple, no holy day is left him any more on earth? What errand can he have up among the clouds, while yet no heaven arches above his soul?

Peer Holm eventually finds peace in the contemplation of man's undaunted spirit, which dwarfs, in Peer's eyes, his material accomplishments.

Disillusionment with the engineer dates back as early as 1912, the year in which Willa Cather wrote *Alexander's Bridge,* a fictionalized account of the collapse of the Quebec bridge which occurred in 1905. Her hero, Bartley Alexander, seems at first to be cast in an heroic mold.

> When Alexander reached the library door, he switched on the lights and stood six feet and more in the archway, glowing with strength and cordiality and rugged, blond good looks. There were other bridge builders in the world, certainly, but it was always Alexander's picture that the Sunday Supplement men wanted, because he looked as a tamer of rivers ought to look. Under his tumbled sandy hair his head seemed as hard and powerful as a catapult, and his shoulders looked strong enough in themselves to support a span of any one of his ten great bridges, that cut the air above as many rivers.

But soon ominous overtones begin to intrude, suggesting flaws behind the imposing facade. Alexander finds that he cannot cope with an inner turbulence, and he drifts into a liaison with an actress which saps his will and threatens to destroy his marriage and his career. He has undertaken a great cantilever bridge in Canada, "the most important piece of bridge building going on in the world," but the "strong and sullen" man within gives him no peace and bids fair to overwhelm him completely. At the crucial point in his personal disintegration, Alexander's great bridge collapses and carries him to his death.

A man, Willa Cather tells us, and by implication a society, may be outwardly strong and materially productive, and yet simultaneously tortured by the darker forces of the human spirit. Such a man, or society, is as inadequately designed as the great symbolic bridge which collapsed so spectacularly into the waters of a Canadian river. Perhaps our entire civilization, dedicated as it is to material pursuits, is destined for such a catastrophe.

Other writers have found the engineer to be a convenient character through whom to exhibit various inadequacies of human nature. In Warwick Deeping's story, *The Great Saaba Bridge,* an engineer is depicted as an emotionally impoverished creature, obsessed with his work, driven by ambition, and totally unsuited for love and marriage. John O'Hara tops this by making the central character of his story, *The Engineer,* a fraud and a homosexual. In A. Den Doolard's novel, *The Land Behind God's Back,* an engineer is shown to be politically naïve and selfishly engrossed with his own work, even as his country suffers the torments of war. Finally, enlisted as a partisan, he destroys in the line of duty the bridge which is his most cherished creation, acknowledging at last his obligation as a citizen and human being. In *The Magicians* J. B. Priestley pities his inhibited engineer who knows "just enough to build walls round himself—not enough to make door and windows." The engineer hero of Stephen Becker's *The Outcasts* returns home after building a bridge in the tropical jungle, resigned to being "the same pulpy blind slug with a white underbelly and traveller's checks."

And in *The Magic Mountain* Thomas Mann selects an engineer to be the innocent and naïve foil around whom swirls the intellectual discourse of the significant characters. "Mediocre" is the word that Mann uses to describe his befuddled engineer protagonist.

All these authors are saying, each in his own way, that even if engineering is not actually malignant in its effects on human life, it is at best beside the point. No matter what men contrive to ease their lot, they must suffer and die, and true wisdom consists of seeking to relate humbly and meaningfully to the universe and to our fellow men. The admonition is as old as the story of the tower of Babel.

Hero or villain?

What are we to make of the conflicting portraits of the engineer with which we find ourselves confronted? The first temptation, based primarily on the caliber of the writing in each of the two camps, is to conclude that shallow and naïve authors are enthusiastic admirers of the engineer, and writers of depth and sensitivity are his severest critics.

In support of this theory we can even point to two novels which worship the engineer in terms so alien to the liberal traditions of Western thinking as to be distasteful. *Wild River* by Anna Louise Strong is a Communist-oriented novel dealing with the building of a dam on Russia's Dnieper River, and in it the engineer appears as a faceless culture hero dedicated to the state. Many current Russian novels are of the same sort. On the other hand, in Ayn Rand's *Atlas Shrugged* the engineer hero is possessed by a neofascistic creed of selfishness which holds that the strong should rightfully dominate the earth. If a man is known by his friends, such friends do not speak well for the engineer.

But a clear-cut delineation along the lines of "good" writers and "bad" is bound to elude us. As a matter of fact, if we penetrate deep enough into the inner sanctum of literature, past the good authors to the truly great, we find support for the engineer in two very unexpected quarters.

First let us turn to *Faust,* Goethe's famous drama of modern man's search for fulfillment. The plot of Part I of this classic is universally familiar. Faust, jaded with every experience that life can offer him, wagers his soul with the devil that he will never experience a moment so satisfying that he will say, "Ah linger on, thou art so fair!" Mephistopheles tempts him with youth, knowledge, magical powers and other assorted pleasures, including the most beautiful and pure of women, but Faust cannot shed his discontent. Part II of the drama, which was written in the wisdom of Goethe's old age, and published after his death, is not nearly so dramatic as Part I, and for this reason is not nearly so widely read. But the fact is that in Part II Faust finally *does* find the moment of complete satisfaction for which he has been searching all his life. He experiences this moment while participating in a dike-building and land-reclamation project!

One literary critic has commented that "to some readers it may seem strange and even flat that Faust should find his highest happiness in a more or less prosaic engineering project."[2] But Goethe's solution for the dilemma of his hero stands for all to read and ponder. Although in finding his moment of complete satisfaction, Faust loses his bet with the devil, his soul is saved, since "whoever aspiring, struggles on, for him there is salvation."

In Franz Kafka's allegorical novel, *The Castle,* written in 1920, modern man reappears, searching for he knows not what. A hundred years have passed since Goethe's Faust impetuously assaulted the gates of heaven, and Kafka's bewildered protagonist, K., only dimly remembers what his heroic predecessor learned so well. K. strives stubbornly to attain recognition from the mysterious mountaintop "castle," but his every effort is thwarted. In his confusion he is certain of only one thing, that he has been appointed to a particular post in the castle hierarchy, and it is clear that his salvation hinges on his receiving confirmation of this appointment. The job which he seeks with all the wit and strength he possesses is that of *land surveyor*. Through chaos Kafka seems dimly the possibility of man's salvation in his continued application to honest and productive tasks.

After reading Goethe and Kafka we can no longer even speculate that the authors of greatest sensitivity are inclined to be most hostile to engineering. And yet we are reluctant to attribute the striking differences we have observed to nothing more significant than individual variations in temperament and taste.

The historical view

Perhaps we can escape from our dilemma by viewing in historical context the writers whom we have considered. Indeed, in the deepened perspective of history all appears suddenly clear.

In primitive and poverty-stricken societies, engineering, once its purpose is understood, is esteemed, even venerated. Few peoples, at least in the Western world, are so passive and stoical that they will not exert themselves to ease their physical discomfort if the means are available. The awakening of a somnolent society by a technological leap forward is always an exciting event. Before art, before philosophy, even before religion, men want food and protection from the elements, and they want to see their families free from pain and fear. Working toward these goals is at once demanding and rewarding. In many respects the pioneer represents man at his best and most exhilarated. So it is only fitting and to be expected that pioneering societies should have their heroes, and that engineers should be amongst the foremost of these heroes, and that the storytellers should proudly recount their deeds.

But pioneering days do not last indefinitely. Slowly but surely the wealth of a society increases and the physical lot of the people improves. It is *then* that philosophers and artists begin to wonder why contentment is not increasing in proportion to improving living conditions. They see that health and wealth have not brought happiness, and worse, that in the pursuit of health and wealth some of the ameliorating features of the old life have been lost. It is at this point that a feeling of betrayal sets in. In retrospect the old ways suddenly seem better than the new, and the philosophers and artists lament the loss of tradition, innocence, and awe.

The problem goes far beyond the activities or preferences of either engineers or artists, right to the heart of the tragic human condition. Men are so constituted that they crave sustenance and comfort. Evolution has blessed them with intelligence and inventiveness and curiosity. Yet since the beginning of history men have deplored the losses which accompany each step along the road of progress. The myths of Adam and Eve and Pandora's box make this clear. But the Paradise of innocence cannot be regained merely by rejecting the fruits of progress. In this respect history is irreversible. So modern man looks about desperately for the resolution of his dilemma.

Goethe, as we have seen, has Faust, after searching heaven and earth, find salvation in an engineering project. But this is not the carefree engineering of the pioneer nor the callous engineering of the materialist. It is engineering transfigured—transfigured by concern for one's fellow man and by reverence for the universal harmony.

All creative artists, no matter how refined their sensibilities, must come to realize in the end that man is a maker as well as a dreamer, and that if he were to reject completely his earthly pursuits, his life would become intolerably barren. Art and religion may grace his days but they cannot fill them. This is what Kafka's bewildered K. senses. From his cerebral wasteland he perceives dimly the need to return in some fashion to the brick-and-mortar existence of his forebears.

Toward a new literature
of engineering

The world is waiting for a new literature. Following the insights of Goethe and Kafka it must seek to synthesize the practical, technological activities of man with his emotional and spiritual needs. At this point in history we should have learned once and for all that if either of these aspects of man's nature is neglected, it is neglected only to his peril and impoverishment.

C. P. Snow has made an interesting sortie into this uncharted territory with his series of novels about those English scientists who are relentlessly invading the "corridors of power." As scientifically trained men rise in the establishment, the social order changes, and the ways of the world must soon reflect these changes. Shifting social patterns traditionally provide an excellent spawning ground for fiction, and it is likely that others will soon follow where Snow has led.

But Snow pointedly excludes engineers from his select scientific fraternity. In *The New Men* he discusses the "rift in technical society," and makes it quite clear where his sympathies lie.

> The engineers . . . the people who made the hardware, who used existing knowledge to make something go, were in nine cases out of ten, conservatives in politics, acceptant of any regime in which they found themselves, interested in making their machine work, indifferent to long-term social guesses.
>
> Whereas the physicists, whose whole intellectual life was spent in seeking new truths, found it uncongenial to stop seeking when they had a look at society. They were rebellious, questioning, protestant, curious for the future and unable to resist shaping it. The engineers buckled to their jobs and gave no trouble, in America, in Russia, in Germany; it was not from them, but from the scientists, that came heretics, forerunners, martyrs, traitors.

Of course, Snow's view is not necessarily definitive. It may be true that engineers are not flamboyantly challenging the power structure of the world; but their presence in the world is being felt nevertheless. And this presence will inevitably find expression in meaningful literature. Some tentative efforts in this direction are already being made.

The altruistic engineer

The Ugly American, by Eugene Burdick and William J. Lederer, tells of an engineer who, in a simple and supremely decent way, assists people in an economically underdeveloped part of the world. The great adventure of technological assistance to the poorer nations is certainly a worthy subject for exploration by novelists of the future. In *The 480,* Burdick carries this theme to almost ludicrous extremes by having his engineer hero prevent a war between India and Pakistan, thereby becoming an internationally acclaimed hero and nearly president of the United States. *The Ugly American* and *The 480* are not great novels by any means. But they are an indication of themes that are in the air, themes that we are sure to hear again.

Roll back the sea

The new literature of engineering need not concern itself exclusively with matters of worldwide political and economic importance. Another example of this new literature, quite different in tone and intent, is *Roll Back the Sea* by the Dutch author, A. Den Doolard. This novel tells the story of the rebuilding of the dikes of Holland's Walcheren Island after they had been destroyed during World War II. It is the story of a gallant people, and, more specifically, it is the story of the *Waterstaat* engineers, the "water wizards" who fight Holland's never-ending battle against the sea. The story revolves primarily about the doings of Chief Engineer Andre van Hummel, a man who is small and waspish, but great because of his knowledge of his profession and the strength of his dedication. Yet this is not merely a tale about a good engineer. The simple folk of the land —fearful and suspicious, but long-suffering and brave—play their part. Rascal contractors appear, drawn by the lure of profit; but their greed seems insignificant compared with their skill and energy, for "profit is merely the bait that destiny has offered to these calculators." A vast gamut of human experience is run, from petty moments of computation to thrilling moments of high adventure. Dominating all is the unrelenting force of nature, brutish and terrifying yet awesome and intoxicating. Several threads running through this book may prove to be recurring themes in the new literature under discussion.

First is the assumption that the professional man is a social animal who finds his moments of greatest satisfaction in sharing achievements with his fellows. This satisfaction is not purely self-effacing; it includes legitimate pride in one's individual worth. Yet it is vastly different from the ever-elusive gratification which so many characters in modern fiction seek feverishly to find within their barren "selves."

Second is the acceptance of the fact that much of the average man's life must consist of ordinary days, lacking in excitement and drama, and that these days of calm are relieved by relatively few days of private and public glory. When life has been too long serene it can become dull, but even the dullest days can be spiced with the memory of some great event through which one has lived, or the dream of a great moment which lies in the future. This acceptance of a natural ebb and flow of passion in human affairs is also a departure from the feverish search for perpetual exaltation which is portrayed in many modern novels.

Third, we find an antiquated but strangely refreshing attitude toward connubial love. In contemporary fiction, and particularly in contemporary drama, men and women are forever seeking release from their anxieties in a turning toward each other—in the pure magic of intense and endlessly rhapsodic "love." But, according to Doolard, "there is not a man in all Holland who will not leave his family when the water calls." This is not to say that the men do not love their women. On the contrary, the man whose life is enriched with a "calling" is better able to love fully and is more likely to be loved in return. The man who brings nothing to love but his interest in love itself makes as poor a mate as he is a man.

A fourth and dominant theme is the salutary effect of a continuing physical challenge on the vitality and morale of a society. In this sense the Dutch are fortunate to have the sea as an adversary. All men grow in stature as they carve out their bits of fertile land in defiance of the elements. This is a tragic view of life in that it implies that if we should ever achieve all of our goals, we would be desolate. But the tragedy becomes muted once we realize that we can never run out of obstacles to test our mettle. And it is a noble view in that man locked in proud battle with the universe is a noble sight.

Albert Camus has written of Sisyphus, who was condemned by the gods to ceaselessly roll a rock to the top of a mountain only to see it roll to the bottom again, that one must imagine him happy; "the struggle itself toward the heights is enough to fill a man's heart."

Or, as Doolard puts it in his introduction to *Roll Back the Sea,* we should not lament the fact that man won only a transitory victory in

> . . . the fifteen long and bitter months when he fought the sea for that grain of the cosmos called Walcheren. . . . And what matter if that grain is washed away tomorrow by the tide of time? In all eternity man has defended it amid wind and water; for all eternity, in this little corner of the universe, he has dealt the sea its greatest defeat.

Salvation in ingenuity

A literary work need not deal explicitly with professional engineers in order to say something of importance about engineering.

Faust and K. are certainly not engineers in any usual sense of the word. Technological man can be represented symbolically by a protagonist who at first glance appears to be someone quite different. This is the case in *The Woman in the Dunes*, a jewel-like, allegorical novel by the Japanese author Kobo Abé.

A young man, trapped by a woman who lives at the bottom of a sand pit, reaches the ultimate in despair. There is no escape, and life appears to be a meaningless routine of bare survival. The people from a nearby village force him to dig sand perpetually, withholding his water supply when he does not comply with their orders. One day he discovers that he can obtain fresh water from the sand with a simple device based on the principle of capillary action. He has now achieved some small degree of independence in the face of a hostile universe. He busies himself with calculations and experiments, and begins to find contentment in the daily routine that had previously seemed abhorrent. Finally given the opportunity to escape, he decides to remain. He has found happiness where it was least expected, in the ritual of survival, the age-old ritual of proving his humanity by the use of his ingenuity. The *activity* of engineering—not merely its fruits—has shown the way to salvation in the midst of the apparent desolation of modern life.

Technology and faith

The Woman in the Dunes is written against a backdrop of agnosticism and despair; but acceptance of a technological world need not mean abandonment of faith. Engineering and religion are not mutually antagonistic; technology and spirituality are joined by bonds which are strong in spite of the fact that they have never been clearly defined.

The Spire, by English novelist William Golding, explores these bonds. Set in medieval England, it tells the story of the building of a cathedral tower, a tower which threatens to cause the collapse of the structure on which it rests. Priest and master builder confront each other, and the construction is accompanied by their dialogue, the dialogue between faith and technology. At one point the priest addresses the master builder in these words:

> My son. The building is a diagram of prayer; and our spire will be a diagram of the highest prayer of all. God revealed it to me in a vision, his unprofitable servant. He chose me. He chooses you, to fill the diagram with glass and iron and stone, since the children of men require a thing to look at. D'you think you can escape? You're not in my net— . . . It's His. We can neither of us avoid this work. And there's another thing. I've begun to see how we can't understand it either, since each new foot reveals a new effect, a new purpose.

Not only cathedrals, but every great work of man is an expression of motivation and of purpose which cannot be completely divorced from religious implications. By drawing particular attention to this, *The Spire* makes an important contribution to contemporary literature.

The future of engineering in fiction

The simple praising and damning of the engineer in fiction must yield, amongst serious writers, to a more complex view of the role of technology in life. A certain hostility toward science and materialistic pursuits is endemic in the literary community, and by the nature of things must always remain so. Yet we have seen some of the ways in which a new literature of engineering may develop, and have considered several themes already being explored: the rise of men of science into the power elite (Snow); the altruistic impulse of engineers in assisting underdeveloped nations (Burdick and Lederer); the tranquil satisfactions of the professional life and the stimulating effect of the challenges of nature (Doolard); the elemental pleasures of ingenuity (Abé); the bonds between technology and faith (Golding). The future treatment of engineering in literature should be fascinating indeed.

Engineers as writers

There is one thing, however, that we engineers have little reason to expect from creative writers, present or future, and this is a precise and meaningful description of our actual professional activities. For details of engineering activities we must look to other engineers, engineers who can write. There are many such men who are worth reading, from Frontinas and Agricola to Smeaton and Hoover, but since they are coprofessionals, not creative artists, they do not come within the scope of our present study.

When engineers attempt to write creatively—there have been a few attempts at novels and poetry—the results are usually disastrous.

Science fiction

There is science fiction, to be sure, but this is more an entertainment created by scientifically trained men than it is a true branch of literature. This is a statement likely to evoke protest, particularly among engineers, many of whom are science fiction devotees. After all, is not science fiction, as a leading editor in the field proclaims, "a perfectly natural outgrowth of the true nature of our culture?"[3] And does it not cast engineers in gallant roles? (It is not concerned with stuffy civil engineers, the traditional builders that seem to interest traditional writers, but rather with electronics and rocket men, honest-to-goodness space-age engineers.)

Admittedly science fiction is a cultural phenomenon of importance. Certainly it can be fun, instructive, and chock-full of interesting political and philosophical statements. Science fiction of the past, particularly that of Jules Verne, is historically significant and has a certain charm. But science fiction can not be considered *literature* until it is written by outstanding literary artists. Many prominent nineteenth-century writers dabbled in fantasy, and in our own time we have the speculations about the future in Aldous Huxley's *Brave New World* and George Orwell's *1984*. But these works have been outside of the mainstream of literary concern. Besides, such works have little or nothing to do with the character or condition of the engineer as such, and so are not really within our present area of interest.

Is it possible that science fiction will one day mature into a truly esteemed art form, interpreting for the world not only the technological wonders of today and the future but also the quality of life in the scientific and engineering communities? "Regrettably," admits a leading science-fiction writer, "not too many people have both extensive scientific training and intensive literary training—and good speculative fiction calls for both."[4] We might add that significant literature requires more than literary training, no matter how intensive. It requires talent and a spark of artistic genius that is not readily found among men in the scientific professions.

Well then, comes the logical reply, let us teach science to our creative writers. But, as Aldous Huxley has pointed out in his beautiful little book, *Literature and Science*, men of letters have never written with any great enthusiasm about the actual substance of science and technology—the theories and techniques —and indeed when they have tried, their observations have often been inaccurate and silly, and eventually become dated and grotesque. I think that we can take Huxley's word for it that true novelists and poets are not likely to be passionately interested in science and technology *as such*. Rather "their concern has been mainly with the social and psychological consequences of advancing technology."[5]

New horizons of awareness

Novelists will not teach us engineering, nor can we even count on them to write about our engineering accomplishments as well as we can do this ourselves. But creative writers can tell us much about ourselves and our way of life that we might otherwise never comprehend.

Inscribed on the ancient Temple of Apollo at Delphi was the maxim, "Know thyself." Most sages have agreed that this is the beginning of wisdom. The creative writer helps us toward this end and beckons us toward ever new horizons of awareness.

Recommended reading

Anyone interested in studying the development of the engineer as a protagonist in literature will want to read the books considered in this chapter pretty much in the order that they are mentioned. Most readers, however, will only want to sample here and there, and the following comments are intended to help them choose judiciously.

Unfortunately, three of the outstanding works mentioned in this chapter are currently out of print. However, they are available in most libraries and are well worth seeking out. They are: Johan Bojer, *The Great Hunger* (Grosset & Dunlap, 1919); A. Den Doolard, *Roll Back the Sea* (Simon and Schuster, 1948); Rudyard Kipling, "The Bridge-Builders," in *The Day's Work* (Doubleday & McClure, 1898).

Of those books readily available in bookshops, Willa Cather, *Alexander's Bridge* (Bantam Books HC161) and John Hersey, *A Single Pebble* (Bantam Books FC248) make a good introduction to this field for the average engineer. Both authors are well-known, albeit minor, literary figures; their styles are simple and direct, and both books are fairly short.

The following three excellent contemporary novels are a little more formidable, but still present no special problems. Kobo Abé, *The Woman In the Dunes* (Berkley S1104); William Golding, *The Spire* (Harvest Books HB94); and C. P. Snow, *The New Men* (Scribner SL33).

Interesting and easy to digest, although lacking in literary distinction are: Eugene Burdick and William J. Lederer, *The Ugly American* (W. W. Norton N305); Eugene Burdick, *The 480* (Dell 2684); James Michener, *Caravans* (Bantam Books N2830); John O'Hara, "The Engineer," in *The Cape Cod Lighter* (Bantam Books W2718).

Of historical interest mainly, although fun in a way: Zane Grey, *The U. P. Trail* (Pocket Books C231).

Good adventure novels featuring engineers: Pierre Boulle, *The Bridge Over the River Kwai* (Bantam Books FP26) and Elleston Trevor, *The Flight of the Phoenix,* (Avon V2144).

For Ayn Rand admirers only: her *Atlas Shrugged* (Signet Books Y2823). Goethe's *Faust* and Kafka's *The Castle* are mentioned prominently in this chapter, and they are both acknowledged literary masterpieces. However, they are not recommended for reading in the present context. Their relationship to engineering is tangential and philosophical, and they are two works that are, for the average reader, more interesting to talk about than they are to read.

For those interested in science fiction a highly recommended introduction and anthology is H. Bruce Franklin, *Future Perfect, American Science Fiction of the Nineteenth Century* (Oxford University Press, 1966). Among the most popular contemporary writers in the science fiction field, each with many titles to his credit are: Isaac Asimov, Ray Bradbury, Arthur C. Clarke, and Robert A. Heinlein. A fine, new translation of Jules Verne's *Twenty Thousand Leagues Under the Sea* has been done by Walter J. Miller (Washington Square Press, 1966).

Engineer authors are well represented and intelligently discussed in Walter J. Miller and Leo E. A. Saidla (eds.), *Engineers as Writers* (D. Van Nostrand, 1953). Also of interest: *Engineering*, an anthology edited by Samuel Rapport and Helen Wright (Washington Square Press, W852); John R. Whinnery (ed.), *The World of Engineering* (McGraw-Hill, 1965); Albert Love and James Saxon Childers (eds.), *Listen to Leaders in Engineering* (Tupper and Love, David McKay Company, 1965).

Even farther afield, but worthy of mention at this point, is the interesting anthology, *Scientists as Writers* edited by James Harrison (M.I.T. 32).

For discussion of the relationship between science and literature, see the beautiful and poetic *Literature and Science* by Aldous Huxley (Harper & Row, 1963), *The Poet and the Machine* by P. Ginestier (University of North Carolina Press, 1961), and two fine anthologies: John J. Cadden and Patrick R. Brostowin (eds.), *Science and Literature* (D. C. Heath Paperback); and Arthur O. Lewis (ed.), *Of Men and Machines,* (Dutton D130).

CHAPTER FIVE

The World
of Literature

Stretched out before the wayfarer in the world of literature lies a broad highway, straight and smooth, brilliantly illuminated, lined with billboards and directional signs. The name of this highway is "The Great Books," and along its well-marked lanes have journeyed hundreds of thousands of students.

The great books versus new vistas

Nothing would be easier for any guide than to follow this route, that is, simply to list the great books and to recommend them to the reader. And nothing could be safer, since there are a half dozen or so authoritative lists, all generally in agreement with one another. Essentially these lists reflect the judgement that a third of the world's great literature was written by the ancient Greeks and Romans, and almost all of the remaining two-thirds before the mid-nineteenth century.

To follow this course would be a disservice, I am convinced, to the engineer seeking a meaningful introduction to literary experience. For there are many literary byways worth exploring, although they have not been sanctioned by respected authorities. More important, in our own time there are many new trails being blazed which reveal vistas scarcely dreamed of by the writers of antiquity.

By the use of the highway metaphor I do not mean to imply that the great books are dull or dry or tedious. They are rich and diverse and magnificent, and they form the core of our cultural heritage. But the plain truth is that, for all their prestige, many of them have an appeal that is primarily historical; their message has become more traditional than vital. As the compilers of at least one "100-best" list have acknowledged, they are more aptly termed "significant" than "great."

The classics and today's reader

Is this heresy? If we view the matter pragmatically, most of the classics are clearly not the books that are most popular with the majority of today's intelligent readers. Nor are they the books most likely to attract and hold new readers, since difficulty of content and strangeness of style are often obstacles to the uninitiated. Also—and perhaps this is the crucial factor from our present point of view—many works which seem splendid and rewarding in *group* study are much less so when tackled by the individual reader. It is one thing to sit in a class and talk *about* such greats as Virgil, Dante, Rabelais, Milton, and Goethe, to mention just a few. It is quite another thing for the solitary reader to pick up a book by one of these gentlemen and to start to read it through.

Let us agree that "the great books" *are* truly worthy of study. But let us recognize also that there are works of our era which speak to us with more immediacy, and which deserve our attention. By "our era" in literature I mean to include the entire lifetime of the novel, roughly the past two hundred years. If we were to restrict ourselves to works of our own generation, we would be foolishly depriving ourselves of too many treasures. Indeed, there are admirers of "modern literature" who would have us eliminate our own generation altogether, authorities in whose eyes great modern literature ended with the death of Marcel Proust in 1922. But we need not be intimidated by these magistrates of taste any more than by the single-minded champions of the ancient classics.

From antiquity to the contemporary scene

Let us not dwell on our predicament, but rather proceed in what seems to be the most advantageous way, considering our own particular needs. Let us review the main creative periods of literature, and reacquaint ourselves with the great literary figures. At the very least let us know them by name and reputation. Let us stop along the way where a stop is indicated—some stops we must agree are essential—and then move along quickly.

Having passed through antiquity, the Middle Ages, the Renaissance, and well into the Age of Reason, we will come upon the beginnings of the novel, the literary form which has taken a central position in our culture. Let us review the most noteworthy novels—English, Continental, and American—and attempt to select a few which will make the most rewarding reading. Let us then see what modern literature has to offer us, and finally look about at the contemporary scene.

The Book of Books

For Western man, great literature begins with the Bible. Written between the thirteenth century B.C. and the third century A.D., the "Book of Books" is really a collection of books—a compilation of stories, biographies, letters, orations, prayers, poems, and essays which constitute a literary treasure as well as a sacred text. Great plots, psychological insight, moral intelligence, beautiful style—everything that we associate with outstanding literature is present in abundance. The Creation, the Garden of Eden, the Fall of Man, the Murder of Abel by Cain, Noah and the Ark, the Tower of Babel, Abraham and Isaac, Jacob and Esau, Joseph and his Brothers, Moses and the Escape from Egypt, the Ten Commandments, Joshua at Jericho, David and Goliath—these are just a few of the dozens of stories that have become a part of each one of us. The New Testament has less variety of theme, but its memorable scenes—the Sermon on the Mount, the Last Supper, the Crucifixion—have also become an integral part of our literary inheritance.

Any meaningful study of literature should start with at least a partial rereading of the Bible.

Homer's Iliad

Out of the depths of the past has come to us another great work compounded of history and legend, attributed to a genius about whose life we know nothing. Homer's *Iliad* tells of the siege of Troy by the Greeks, an event which is thought to have taken place during the twelfth century B.C., perhaps three hundred years before the *Iliad* was created.

The mighty Achilles is the central character among the warring nobles depicted in this epic poem. He is truly a majestic warrior hero, and as he sulks, grieves, rages, and repents, the intensity of his emotion is awesome to behold. "The wrath of

Achilles" has become the ultimate wrath, against which pettier angers pale by comparison.

Homer's other great narrative poem, the *Odyssey*, tells the story of the return home of Odysseus after the Trojan war, his amazing adventures while traveling, and his triumph over his enemies upon his arrival. Whereas Achilles is a man of passion who bravely faces his inevitable death in battle, Odysseus is a man of moderation who prevails because of prudence and intelligence. Both men were heroes to the Greeks.

Hebrews and Greeks

In the Bible, glory is attributed only to God; in Homer it is the prize most sought by men. To the ancient Hebrews the most admired characteristic was righteousness; to the ancient Greeks it was nobility.

As we look back into the past, we can see that we are descendants of both the Greeks and the Hebrews; we are sons of Achilles and Odysseus as well as of the patriarchs and the prophets. Our ancestral homeland is both along the rocky Mediterranean coast and in the parched deserts of the Near East.

As engineers, it is particularly interesting for us to note the respect with which material "things" are treated by the ancients. In the *Iliad* the scepter of Agamemnon, the shield of Ajax, and the bow of Pandarus are lovingly described. Not only their shape and texture but their manufacture and history are considered significant. There is importance and dignity in the robing of a warrior, in the serving of a feast. In the early parts of the Bible, also, there is an earthy materialism side by side with exalted spirituality. We find there an unashamed relish for such things as cattle and grain, bricks and planks, jewels and tunics.

Disdain for material things was to appear soon enough in both the Greek and Judeo-Christian traditions. But it is good for us to remember that before men fell under the spell of idealistic philosophies and guilt-ridden theologies, they maintained a natural and healthy relationship to the physical world about them.

The *Iliad,* like the Bible, is required reading. Happily the dramatic qualities which have kept it a favorite for almost three thousand years commend it to us still. It is not a book that needs to be read straight through. Chronologically it is somewhat disjointed, and there are portions dealing with the Olympian gods which seem a little silly. However each of the twenty-four chapters, or "books," is clearly subtitled, and the work can be read selectively. The verse translation by Richmond Lattimore is excellent. For those who find the poetry more of a hindrance than a source of pleasure, the prose translation by W. H. D. Rouse is recommended.

The Golden Age of Greece

During the Golden Age of Greece, which began in the fifth century B.C., literature held a place of importance which has no parallel in history. Poetry received public and official recognition, and was customarily presented in contests at national festivals. Dramatists, also, competed for highly regarded prizes, presenting their plays in large theaters before influential and attentive audiences. Philosophy, history, and oratory were esteemed and studied by the leaders of the community. Under these conditions the profusion of great literary works is understandable. What has come down to us through the ages is a considerable body of literature, although much has been lost. In heroic poetry, philosophy, history, and oratory we have most of what the Greeks themselves regarded as their best. In lyric poetry and in drama, however, there survives only a very small portion of what we know existed.

Greek philosophy, particularly that of Plato, can be justly categorized as creative literature. But, for the sake of order, we will postpone consideration of the philosophers until we come to philosophy, in Chapters 6 and 7.

There are even more compelling reasons for considering the Greek historians as literary figures, rather than recorders of history. Herodotus (484?–?425 B.C.) mixed a charming but semi-mythical view of the distant past with a biased pro-Athens account of the Persian Wars. He came to be called "Father of Lies." Thucydides (460?–?400 B.C.) wrote an "eyewitness" contemporary history of the Peloponnesian War, but he also sacrificed historical accuracy for the sake of making his point. "The paradox is that to give meaning to history he tended to abandon history."[1]

Herodotus and Thucydides are on many a "must" list, and the niche they occupy in the history of letters is an important one. Honored through hundreds of generations, their credentials are impressive. But extensive reading in their histories is only for the man who has read much else first, or for the man who has unlimited time at his disposal.

The tragedies of Aeschylus, Sophocles, and Euripides

The Greek dramatists, however, are a different matter. They cannot be passed by with brief acknowledgment; here we must stop and pay homage. The tragedies of Aeschylus (525–456 B.C.), Sophocles (496?–406 B.C.), and Euripides (480?–406 B.C.) are among the most sublime achievements of mankind. It always sounds odd when one hears it said that great tragedies are not saddening but, on the contrary, uplifting. Yet this happens to be the case. The tragic view of life is not a happy one, to be sure, since it sees man subject to forces beyond his control and faced with inevitable death. But in the hands of a dramatic genius it leads to inspiration rather than despair. A classical scholar has explained it thus:

If in the elemental struggle against destiny man seems doomed to defeat, that is the way life looked to the tragedians. Their gloom is no fatalistic pessimism but an adult confrontation of reality, and their emphasis is not on the grimness of life but on the capacity of great figures to adequate themselves to it.[2]

The best known, and perhaps the most perfectly wrought, Greek tragedy, is Sophocles' *Oedipus Rex*. Unwittingly, Oedipus the king fulfills a dire prophecy by murdering his father and marrying his mother, from whom he has been separated since infancy. In a modern sense he is guiltless, since he does not know the facts about what he has done; yet the "fatal flaws" in his character, impetuousness and immoderate passion, are instrumental in bringing about his downfall. The drama ends with the hero overcome by grief and shame, blinded by his own hand, and banished from his country, yet ennobled in his agony. In Oedipus, as in all great tragedy, the audience is moved both to "pity" and to "fear." But in the end we experience a "catharsis," which purges us of these emotions and reconciles us to the hero's fate and to our own.

We must read at least this one tragedy. The Greek dramas are quite short compared with plays of today, scarcely fifty pages on an average, and if *Oedipus* serves to whet the appetite, other masterpieces are *The Oresteia*, a trilogy by Aeschylus, and *Antigone* by Euripides. For the engineer, a drama of particular interest is Aeschylus's *Prometheus Bound*, dealing with the cruel punishment meted out to the Titan who brought fire and technology into the world in defiance of the orders of the great god Zeus.

Other notables of Greek literature

After having resolved not to be intimidated by the "great books" approach, we have already acknowledged that there are three masterworks of antiquity which cannot be ignored: the

Bible, the *Iliad,* and at least one of the Greek tragedies. In Chapter 7 we will say the same about Plato. But from this point on we can afford to be resolute; like Odysseus, let us tie ourselves to the mast so that we will not be lured by the sirens. Until we reach Shakespeare in the sixteenth century, there is not another genius for whom we *must* stop. There are many to whom we may wish to return some day, and with whom we want some acquaintance as we move along.

Among the other notables of Greek literature (excluding the philosophers, whom we will meet in Chapter 7), perhaps the most famous is Aesop (sixth century B.C.), teller of fables. Aristophanes (448?–?380 B.C.) is known for his comedies— satirical, bawdy, and fantastic. Most familiar to modern audiences and students is his *Lysistrata,* in which the women seek an end to war by going on a sex strike. Hesiod (eighth century B.C.) and Apollonius (third century B.C.) were outstanding epic poets. The lyric poetry of Sappho (seventh century B.C.) has enchanted each succeeding generation. The essays and biographies of Plutarch (46?–?120 A.D.) were, until not so long ago, part of every liberal education. His *Lives,* short biographies of prominent Greeks and Romans, inspired schoolboys of the past and can serve to inspire us still.

The literature of Rome

Among the early Romans, the comedies of Plautus (254?– 184 B.C.) and Terence (185?–159 B.C.) were popular. During the "Golden Age" of Latin literature we encounter first the lyric poetry of Catullus (84?–54 B.C.), the military histories of Julius Caesar (100–44 B.C.), and the masterly orations and essays of Cicero (106–43 B.C.). Then, during the reign of Augustus, we come upon Virgil (70–19 B.C.), the most revered of the Roman poets, both during his lifetime and after. His *Aeneid* is a national epic, glorifying Rome and its legendary founding by the patriotic hero Aeneas. The *Aeneid* is, undeni-

ably, a "great book," and has been considered so throughout the
ages. Nevertheless, it is not one of the classics most congenial to
the modern reader. The other greats of Augustan Rome are the
poets Horace (65–8 B.C.) and Ovid (43 B.C.–?17 A.D.), and
the historian Livy (59 B.C.–17 A.D.).

The period following the death of Augustus is frequently
called the "Silver Age" of Latin literature. This is the time of
the tragedian Seneca (4 B.C.?–65 A.D.), the story-tellers
Petronius (died 66 A.D.) and Apuleius (born ca. 125 A.D.), the
epic poets Lucan (39–65 A.D.) and Statius (45?–?96 A.D.),
the encyclopedist Pliny the Elder (23?–79 A.D.), his nephew,
the orator Pliny the Younger (61?–113 A.D.), the historian
Tacitus (55?–117 A.D.), and the satirists Martial (40?–104 A.D.)
and Juvenal (60?–?140 A.D.).

Much Roman literature is sophisticated, wicked, and witty.
Some of it is noble in sentiment, patriotic, and manly. Taken as
a whole, however, it is inferior to the Greek literature on which
most of it was modeled. The very qualities which made the
Romans outstanding soldiers, builders, and administrators pre-
vented their art from soaring to great heights.

Rome's decline and the Dark Ages

The years of Rome's decline, as we have seen, were the years
of the rise of the Church. A significant work of this period is the
Confessions of St. Augustine (354–430). Although its purpose
was to bring men into the fold of the Church, this book is considered to be perhaps the most magnificent spiritual autobiography ever written. Augustine's moment of conversion, described in the twelfth chapter of Book VIII, is particularly
memorable. However, it is, for today's reader, a dense and difficult book, a milestone rather than an oasis.

As the Western world sank into the Dark Ages after the fall

of Rome, literary creativity all but disappeared. When the spark was rekindled we find, for the first time, literature in the vernacular languages of the several emerging nations. *Beowulf*, an epic poem written in Old English, dates from about the year 725. In France, the *Song of Roland* appeared in the eleventh century. The great German epic *Nibelungenlied* was written about 1200. Bravery, patriotism, and prowess in combat were the traits most acclaimed in those stormy days. Metered verse was the form most suited to a literature that was more often recited from memory than read from the written page.

The Middle Ages

As the medieval world emerged from chaos, the "romance" evolved. This literary form, created by anonymous bards, was characteristically a tale of love, adventure, chivalry, and enchantment. Classical legends about Troy, Aeneas, and Alexander the Great were retold. King Arthur and the Knights of the Round Table were favorite subjects in England, as were Charlemagne and his peers in France. The concepts of chivalry and courtly love which emerged in these works have influenced the relations between men and women in the Western world ever since.

Allegories were popular during the medieval years, and it is in the morality plays of fourteenth-century Europe that we first encounter such characters as Everyman, Good Deeds, Faith, and Mercy.

Dante and Chaucer

The two literary geniuses of the late Middle Ages are Dante Alighieri (1265–1321) and Geoffrey Chaucer (1340?–1400). Their masterworks are, respectively, *The Divine Comedy* and *The Canterbury Tales*. What a study in contrast! Dante's work describes an allegorical voyage through Hell and Purgatory to Paradise. With Chaucer we are invited on a real pilgrimage with as earthy a group of characters as any in literature. Dante's aim is sublime: to show the path to salvation through reason, revelation, and spiritual love for the ideal woman. Chaucer is simply a supreme storyteller.

The Divine Comedy is known as one of the greatest books of Western civilization. The poetry is considered to be glorious, although those of us who do not read Italian must take the word of others about this. It is said to reconstruct the entire world of Dante's time, theological and secular, mythological and scientific; it is said to summarize the Middle Ages and herald the coming of the Renaissance. Yet it is so full of topical references and strange names that it can scarcely be penetrated without special guidance.

We need no assistance in understanding *The Canterbury Tales,* unless we attempt to read it in the original Middle English. It is one of those works which is great but not obscure, precious but not perplexing.

Both Dante and Chaucer are firmly entrenched as members of the pantheon of literary greats. Let us add them to the list of those to whom we would like to return some day.

For now, let us move on out of the Middle Ages, noting in passing the powerful social protest contained in *Piers Plowman,* by William Langland (1332?–?1400), the famous *Travels* of Marco Polo (1254?–1324), and the poems of that historic Parisian rogue, François Villon (1431?–1463).

The Renaissance

Dates are not a clear indication of whether a literary work is medieval or of the Renaissance. As we have noted, the Renaissance started in Italy in the mid-fourteenth century and worked its way north; it did not flower in England until almost two hundred years later. The Italian scholars Petrarch (1304–1374) and Boccaccio (1313–1375) were men of the Middle Ages and at the same time shapers of the Renaissance. Petrarch, particularly, in his rediscovery of ancient manuscripts, and in his devotion to the man-centered classics of antiquity, showed the way to the new "humanism." As a poet he set the pattern for the coming age. His *Sonnets and Songs* have been called the first great literary expression of romantic love. Boccaccio was also a classical scholar, but he is known best for *The Decameron*, 100 zestful tales of intrigue, adventure, and love.

Erasmus (1466–1536) was the leading humanistic scholar of the later Renaissance, and his *In Praise of Folly*, a sweeping satirical condemnation of the ways of the world, has achieved the status of a minor classic. The unabashed egotism of the Renaissance is well expressed in the *Autobiography* of Benvenuto Cellini (1500–1571). The political realism and cynicism of the age are exemplified in *The Prince*, by Niccolo Machiavelli (1469–1527). In the works of Francois Rabelais (1494?–1553), we find satirical attacks on sixteenth-century standards of education and morality expressed in exuberant, farcical tales about the fantastic giants *Gargantua* and *Pantagruel*.

The Renaissance was an age of cynical iconoclasm, but it also was a time of faith in the future. "Immortal God," wrote Erasmus in 1517, "what a world I see dawning! Why can I not grow young again?" This prevailing sense of optimism gave birth to what we have come to know today as "utopian" literature. The original *Utopia*, by Sir Thomas More (1478–1535), was followed by many others, the most notable of which was *The New Atlantis*, by Sir Francis Bacon (1561–1626).

Montaigne—The engaging skeptic

Of all the writers of the Renaissance, there is only one, in my opinion, who speaks directly to us as if he were our contemporary. This is Michel de Montaigne (1533–1592), the urbane Frenchman who went into semiretirement in his thirty-ninth year, and from then until his death wrote a series of remarkable, personal *Essays*. The essays are about nothing in particular and about everything of importance. They ramble aimlessly, but they win over the reader with their frankness and good humor. Montaigne is not rancorous and quick to criticize as were many other writers of his period, nor does he think that he has all the answers. On the contrary, he is essentially a skeptic, and it is his open-mindedness in particular that appeals to us today.

Cervantes and Don Quixote

The coming of the Renaissance to Spain means only one thing to the student of literature: *Don Quixote*. This famous story, written by Miguel de Cervantes Saavedra (1547–1616), has captured the world's imagination and become part of our folklore. The tale of the Knight of the Sorrowful Countenance and his squire, Sancho Panza, is at once a satire on chivalry and medieval romances, a fine adventure story, and a comedy. But its lasting appeal is based on the contrast between the Don and Sancho, the never-ending dialogue between idealism and practicality, illusion and reality, the spirit and the flesh. The Don is a fool; he is, in fact, insane. But is he not a saint, and possibly saner than the rest of us?

Unfortunately, when enticed by the legend we approach the book itself, we find that *Don Quixote* is extremely difficult to read. It is over-long, much too leisurely, and full of tedious digressions. We thank Cervantes for creating his immortal characters, but regretfully we must confess that the book does not live up to our expectations. Like the Don, in this instance we are better off with the dream than with the reality.

William Shakespeare

When we speak about the great literature of the English Renaissance, the Elizabethan Age, what we really are referring to is the greatness of Shakespeare. True, the age boasted other talented dramatists, such as Ben Jonson (1572?–1637), Thomas Kyd (1557?–?1595), and Christopher Marlowe (1564–1593), and such outstanding poets as John Donne (1573–1631) and Edmund Spenser (1552–1599). But it was William Shakespeare (1564–1616) whose genius bestows glory on the age and on all English literature.

Shakespeare has had his ups and downs in public and critical favor. To those who want religious comfort or a strong flavor of moral preaching with their literature, he leaves much to be desired. That he was a nonbeliever cannot be doubted:

> Life's but a walking shadow, a poor player
> That struts and frets his hour upon the stage
> And then is heard no more; it is a tale
> Told by an idiot, full of sound and fury,
> Signifying nothing.

But this hard-headed nonbeliever was also the heartiest of yea-sayers. His portrayals of nobility and valor, love and devotion are matchless, and his affirmation of man and his works is ardent.

> What a piece of work is a man! how noble in reason! how infinite in faculty! in form and moving how express and admirable! in action how like an angel! in apprehension how like a god!

With passion he affirmed the Diety in whom he did not really believe.

> God be prais'd, that to believing souls
> Gives light in darkness, comfort in despair.

Unlike lesser artists who single-mindedly hammer away at a small portion of life, chipping off "messages" which they offer up as truth, Shakespeare embraced all of life and prized its infinite variety.

> At Christmas I no more desire a rose
> Than wish a snow in May's new-fangled mirth;
> But like of each thing that in season grows.

He knew that lasting contentment does not exist, that life consists of emotional oscillations.

> And after summer evermore succeeds
> Barren winter, with his wrathful nipping cold;
> So cares and joys abound, as seasons fleet.

He also saw that variety forces upon man the constant exercise of choice between alternatives.

> Who can be wise, amazed, temperate and furious,
> Loyal and neutral, in a moment?

And long before the advent of existentialism and psychology he sensed that philosophical reasoning cannot compete with existential reality.

> The brain may devise laws for the blood, but a hot temper leaps o'er a cold decree.

He had a touch of the wistfulness that attends the wise man who affirms what he cannot believe.

> When my love swears that she is made of truth,
> I do believe her, though I know she lies.

And he had more than a touch of the melancholy that attends the wise man who knows that he lives on the brink of nothingness.

> For he being dead, with him is beauty slain,
> And, beauty dead, black chaos comes again.

Truth, as Shakespeare knew, is black chaos; but beauty, love, and nobility are the glowing falsehoods that keep us from bleak pessimism in the face of that truth.

Which of his plays shall we read? Clearly if we are to choose one, it must be *Hamlet,* perhaps the single most famous literary work in the Western world, with the exception of the Bible. Hamlet, the melancholy prince, is man at the threshold of the modern age. He is man the intellectual, groping for understanding and uncertain about how to set things to right in a mysterious and sinister world. Between Shakespeare's time and our own there lived many men who thought that they had found the key to understanding the world and ordering society. Over the heads of these men we recognize Shakespeare as our truest poet, and Hamlet as our brother.

With Shakespeare's plays reputation is not deceiving. The most famous are the best: *Hamlet, Macbeth, Othello, King Lear, Romeo and Juliet, Antony and Cleopatra,* and *Julius Caesar.* These are all tragedies and all masterpieces. Some of the histories have their tedious passages, and the comedies even more so. But there is scarcely a work written by this genius that does not have the power to thrill us.

Neoclassicism and the Age of Reason

There is a pendulum effect in the arts, as in all the affairs of men. After the liberating thrust of Renaissance literature came an inevitable counterreaction. Formality and respect for authority gradually began to reappear in the world of letters.

We have seen in Chapter 3 that as the religious wars drew to a close in the mid-seventeenth century, the scales of power tipped toward France. From Paris and Versailles a neoclassical style emerged to dominate the continent. Formed under the influence of an absolute monarchy, the essence of this style was restraint, polish, formality, and discipline. Reason was in the ascendance; passion and excessive individuality were in disrepute.

The French classical drama was developed by the tragedians Pierre Corneille (1606–1684) and Jean Racine (1639–1699), and by the comic genius Molière (1622–1673). The witty maxims of the Duc de La Rochefoucauld (1613–1680) and the fables of Jean de La Fontaine (1621–1695) attained great popularity. Although these elegant works retain some of their original sparkle, as a body they have only limited appeal to us today.

Neoclassicism came to England in 1660 with the recall of Charles II following the death of Oliver Cromwell. Many of Charles's courtiers had spent the period of the Cromwell Commonwealth in France, and they brought back with them a taste for all that they had experienced there. The plays of this "Restoration" period are witty and wicked, the poetry clever and satirical, all in tune with the temper of the age. The foremost man of letters in England at this time was John Dryden (1631–1700), dramatist, poet, and literary critic. In the justly famous *Diaries* of Samuel Pepys (1633–1703) there is to be found a wonderful picture of late seventeenth-century England.

The devout Puritans

Also writing during this period was John Milton (1608–1674). His *Paradise Lost* is a famous poetic work dealing with the fall of man as manifested in the story of Adam and Eve. This sublime, religious poem stands out in stark contrast to the brittle and often licentious literature of Milton's contemporaries. An acknowledged masterwork of English literature, *Paradise Lost* would, nevertheless, stand near the head of a current list of unpopular classics. As a poem it has its magnificent passages, but as a narrative it is sluggish going, and is likely to defeat all but the most determined readers.

Another religious work dating from this generally dissolute period is John Bunyan's (1628–1688) *Pilgrim's Progress*, the famous allegory of Christian's journey to salvation. This ponderous-sounding work has a pleasant surprise in store for the reader. It is direct and unpretentious, aglow with faith and sincerity. Both *Pilgrim's Progress* and *Paradise Lost*, although written during the Restoration, reflect the somber and devout sentiments of a Puritanism then in decline.

The elegant eighteenth century

In eighteenth-century England satiric wit and precision of expression reached a perfection hardly, if ever, equalled since. Joseph Addison (1672–1719) and Richard Steele (1672–1729) commented in *The Spectator* on the fashions and foibles of the times. Lord Chesterfield (1694–1774) wrote his urbane *Letters to His Son*. On the stage, *The Beggar's Opera* by John Gay (1685–1732) burlesqued politics, and William Congreve (1670–1729), Oliver Goldsmith (1728–1774), and Richard Sheridan (1751–1816) carried on the tradition of sparkling social comedy. Samuel Johnson (1709–1784)—best known to us today for his acerbic conversation as recorded by his biographer, James Boswell (1790–1795)—ruled the literary London of his time. Jonathan Swift (1667–1745) wrote *Gulliver's Travels*, not as an amusement for children, but as a biting indictment of man's irrational behavior. The essays of Edmund Burke (1729–1797) persuasively stated conservative political sentiments. The glittering, epigrammatic couplets of Alexander Pope (1688–1744) epitomized the spirit of the age.

In France, Denis Diderot (1713–1784) and the other *philosophes* were at work on the monumental *Encyclopédie*, a definitive statement of the skeptical and rational outlook of the Enlightenment. The most esteemed French literary figure of this century was Voltaire (1694–1778). He wrote extensively in every literary form known, and his influence was widespread, although his verbal attacks on snobbery, bigotry, and superstition made him vulnerable to royal disfavor and even exile. Today he is best remembered for *Candide,* a tale which mocks the optimism of many of Voltaire's literary contemporaries, recommending that we "cultivate our garden" and make the best of things in this incredibly stupid and wicked world.

In America the spirit of the eighteenth century is well captured in the *Autobiography* of Benjamin Franklin (1706–1790). The democratic political philosophy which grew out of the Age of Reason finds supreme expression in the writings of Thomas Jefferson (1743–1826) and Thomas Paine (1737–1809), and in *The Federalist Papers* of Madison, Hamilton, and Jay.

It has been said that the "classical" writers of the seventeenth and eighteenth centuries appeal to our heads and not to our hearts. It is true that the literature of this period does not plumb the depths of the human spirit. The newly developing faith in science directed men's attentions away from inner turbulence toward new social possibilities. However, if we are interested in lucidity and wit, intelligence and craftsmanship—and as engineers how can we not be?—the writers of the Age of Reason command our attention. Since no single work towers above the others, the literature of this period lends itself to selective browsing.

The Romantic rebellion

While the Age of Reason and the Enlightenment were at their height, the rebellion of the Romantics was already under way. Starting about 1750 Jean-Jacques Rousseau (1712–1778) spoke out on behalf of the heart, the emotions, and the importance of the individual. His *Confessions, Émile,* and *The Social Contract* are landmarks in soul-searching autobiography, progressive educational theory, and democratic political thinking, re-

spectively. Thought by many to have been an egocentric hypo-
crite, he nevertheless said things that the world was waiting to
hear, and his influence became as widespread as that of his arch-
rival, Voltaire. The Age of Reason had provided the intellectual
background for democratic thinking. Rousseau, and after him
the other Romantics, provided the necessary compassion and
emotional spark. When one thinks of the intellectual ferment
which eventually led to the French Revolution, the name of
Rousseau comes first to mind.

In England, toward the end of the eighteenth century, the
poems of Robert Burns (1759–1796) and William Blake (1757–
1827) gave expression to the smoldering embers of passion; and
as the nineteenth century dawned, the fires of Romantic poetry
blazed fiercely. Samuel Taylor Coleridge (1772–1834), William
Wordsworth (1770–1850), George Gordon, Lord Byron (1788–
1824), Percy Bysshe Shelley (1792–1822), and John Keats
(1795–1821)—these five names are known throughout the
civilized world, even to men who would never think of reading
a poem. These great poets are Romanticism incarnate. Their
soaring lyrics encompass all that Romanticism has come to mean
—yearnings of the heart, pangs and ecstasies of love, reverence
for nature, worship of beauty, devotion to art, fervent feelings
of brotherhood, and admiration for individual heroism. For inspiration these impassioned artists looked beyond the ugly cities
of the early industrial revolution to the fields and forests of their
beloved England, back in time over the head of newborn science
to the ages of faith and myth, and most important, down
through the veneer of social custom into the depths of their own
hearts.

Poetry and the engineer

What can one say about Romantic poetry, indeed about poetry
in general, to an audience of engineers in the last third of the

twentieth century? Not much, I fear. We can urge upon each other the reading of epic poetry and prose because such works deal with ideas and people and stories. But the poetry of the last two centuries has been concerned mainly with images and with *feelings*. Like music, talking *about* poetry is a very poor substitute for experiencing it. In the words of Archibald Mac-Leish, "A poem should not mean/But be." The poet wants us to sense the glory, the mystery, and the vibrancy of the universe, and of our own being within this universe. By use of rhythm, rhyme, repetition, meter, imagery—by every means his imagination can conceive—he attempts to make contact with us. Whether he succeeds or not, the world is not likely to be greatly affected, as W. H. Auden admits. "For poetry makes nothing happen: it survives/In the valley of its saying where executives/Would never want to tamper; . . . ."[3]

The time is long past when Shelley could boast that "poets are the unacknowledged legislators of the world." This is certainly not true today, if it ever was. But it is more true than it ever was that, in an age of television and automobiles, we are in danger of losing touch with the real world, of losing our sense of personal identity. "Once the individual loses his naïve at-oneness with the living universe," said D. H. Lawrence, "he falls into a state of fear and tries to insure himself with wealth."[4]

"There is no poetry for the practical man," as John Ciardi has said. "There is poetry only for the mankind of the man who spends a certain amount of his life turning the mechanical wheel . . . ."[5] For the sake of the "mankind" within us, we should resolve to give poetry an occasional hearing.

German Romanticism and Faust

Let us return to the Romantic revolution of the late eighteenth and early nineteenth centuries. At this time the literature of Germany began to mature. The works of Gotthold Ephraim

Lessing (1729–1781) and Friedrich Schiller (1759–1805) received international attention, and Johann Wolfgang Von Goethe (1749–1832) emerged as the Olympian literary figure of the age. In his early plays Goethe exalted the ideal of political freedom. In his novelette, *The Sorrows of Young Werther,* he gave expression to a brooding romantic sentimentality which this immensely popular book helped to make fashionable. But Goethe's reputation—and he is considered by many to rank with Homer, Dante, and Shakespeare—rests mainly on his poetic drama, *Faust.* We have had occasion to discuss this work in the preceding chapter. Faust, as we have noted, concluded his career as a civil engineer reclaiming swampland for the benefit of mankind. But he is better known to the world as the supreme Romantic, the insatiable hero who wants to experience *all.* Modern man is often referred to as "Faustian"—constantly striving, never at ease or content. In Faust we have another archetype, a character, like Don Quixote, who enriches our common culture and our vocabulary as well. But, even more than *Don Quixote,* *Faust* is an extremely difficult and disappointing work for today's reader. Translation is a problem, no doubt, as with Cervantes and Dante. But this cannot be the whole answer, as witness the case of Homer. Let us be grateful for the character and for the legend, even if we steer clear of the book itself.

The coming of the novel

During the eighteenth century, as the battle raged between classical dramatists and Romantic dramatists, classical poets and Romantic poets, little did the combatants realize that both drama and poetry were about to receive a near deathblow from a new art form—the novel.

The rise of the novel parallels the rise of the middle class. Heroic romances and sophisticated, bawdy comedies were not adequate to satisfy the tastes of an increasingly wealthy and powerful class of merchants, bankers, manufacturers, and professionals. A well-turned phrase, a subtle romantic nuance, a clever philosophical or theological point—these were of only limited interest to the bustling, striving, competing members of an increasingly fluid society. A vast new audience—many of them women newly liberated from drudgery—created a demand for a new type of literature. The novel was art's answer to this demand.

A novel is essentially a story about people—not kings or knights or saints or devils—but real honest-to-goodness people, making their way in the real world, improving their social position and failing to do so, making money and losing it, loving, hating, clashing, embracing. The early novelists mapped the social scene of their day and peopled it with characters who, through their behavior in successive adventures, became known to the reader. Later novelists set out to explore "the vast unspoken experience that goes on in us, both simultaneously with our outer life, and in solitude . . . , the labyrinthine realms of inner being."[6]

The novel has no fixed rules. The author may sprinkle his story with ideas and opinions, or attempt to exclude them except as they may be expressed by one of his characters. He may make his own presence felt on every page, or tell his story matter-of-factly, documentarily, as it were. But whatever his method or technique, his objective is to tell us about our fellow men, and thus about ourselves, our ambitions, our motives, our limitations, and our potentialities. Lionel Trilling, one of our leading literary critics, has written about the novel in these words:

> For our time the most effective agent of the moral imagination has been the novel of the last two hundred years. It was never, either aesthetically or morally, a perfect form, and its faults and failures can be quickly enumerated. But its greatness and its practical usefulness lay in its unremitting work of involving the reader himself in the moral life, inviting him to put

his own motives under examination, suggesting that reality is not as his conventional education has led him to see it. It taught us, as no other genre ever did, the extent of human variety and the value of this variety. It was the literary form to which the emotions of understanding and forgiveness were indigenous, as if by the definition of the form itself.[7]

The novel in the eighteenth century

Daniel Defoe (1660–1731) is sometimes referred to as the first novelist, and his *Robinson Crusoe* (1719) and *Moll Flanders* (1722) as the first novels. More often the honor is accorded to Samuel Richardson (1689–1761) and his *Pamela* (1740), on the grounds that Defoe's books are too loosely structured to be considered novels in a modern sense. Today, of course, we are used to "novels" with hardly any structure at all; and long before the eighteenth century there were prose narratives which could well be called novels if we felt so inclined. Refined definitions are of no particular interest to us, so let us not dwell on the matter.

Both *Robinson Crusoe* and *Pamela* were tremendous successes, the former with its solid and resourceful middle-class hero, the latter with its young lady protecting her virtue under trying circumstances. Within a decade of Richardson's success, two other outstanding novelists appeared on the scene: Tobias Smollett (1721–1771), author of the picaresque adventures, *Roderick Random* and *Humphrey Clinker,* and Henry Fielding (1707–1754), author of *Joseph Andrews* and *Tom Jones.* Fielding's genius for construction of plot, pace of narrative, and invention of memorable characters, particularly as displayed in *Tom Jones,* has caused him to be called the first master of the novel. The immortal *Tom Jones,* the rambling tale of a lively young man's adventures, mostly amorous, is fun to read, full of amusing incidents and unforgettable people. It is, however, long and discursive and obviously intended for a more leisurely age than our own.

The earliest novels were devoted to "straight" narrative—the heroes engage in love affairs, fights, chases, and surprising encounters. But in 1760 there appeared the first two volumes of a very different kind of novel. *Tristram Shandy* by Laurence Sterne (1713–1768) has been called one vast digression. Hardly anything seems to happen to the hero, who isn't even born until almost half way through the book. This novel is full of anecdote, incidental essays, and jokes. Yet Uncle Toby, Mr. and Mrs. Shandy, Parson Yorick, and several other characters come alive in their thoughts and conversations, just as Tom Jones and his friends come alive in their adventures. *Tristram Shandy* is whimsical and eccentric and sometimes cloyingly sentimental; it is definitely not to everyone's taste. Yet I have found it, for reasons hard to define, one of the most delightful of all English novels.

Jane Austen and Sir Walter Scott

In the saga of the English novel the early nineteenth century belongs to Jane Austen (1775–1817) and Sir Walter Scott (1771–1832). Miss Austen's novels have been dismissed by some readers as mere comedies of manners, frail and lacking in depth. It is true that her subject matter is restricted to the home life of middle-class people in provincial towns. Good breeding and simple domestic pleasures seem to be the standards by which she measures the world. Yet her books have a subtle charm and wit, and if they do not explore all of human experience, what they do touch on is illuminated by an agreeable and civilized insight. Her most popular book is *Pride and Prejudice,* although some consider *Emma* to be her best.

Compared with Jane Austen's exquisite vignettes, Sir Walter

Scott said that what he wrote were "Big Bow-wow stories." What he really wrote were grand, romantic historical novels. For the knight errant in each of us, *Ivanhoe* still makes exciting reading.

Dickens and Thackeray

By the time Charles Dickens (1812–1870) began to write his novels, the industrial revolution in England was creating intolerable conditions for the lower classes. Under the genteel world of Jane Austen there seethed a vast cauldron of human misery. Dickens is the first prominent novelist in whom we find a concern for social reform. His popularity, of course, has not rested on his social conscience, but rather on his talents as a melodramatic storyteller and delineator of unforgettable characters.

Just about everyone, during his school years, has read some Dickens. Whether it is worthwhile returning in maturity to this most famous of all English novelists is in large measure a matter of taste. His novels are long, his style overly rich by today's standards, and his sentimentality occasionally embarrassing. Yet once we become accustomed to his style—and he is not a difficult writer, by any means—its richness can become pleasing. His way with a story is as good as or better than we might have remembered it, and his psychological insight and philosophical overtones are rewards which we probably missed as youthful readers. Tentatively, I would suggest at least one of his novels as a "must," preferably *Great Expectations, David Copperfield,* or *Bleak House.*

Dickens's great contemporary and rival, William Makepeace Thackeray (1811–1863), wrote only one masterpiece, as opposed to Dickens's many, but it is by general agreement one of the outstanding novels in world literature. Its name: *Vanity Fair.* Becky Sharp, a devilishly clever and unscrupulous young lady makes her way up (and down) the social ladder in a world dominated by wealth and position—and sex. Thackeray is not a crusader like Dickens. He reacts to hypocrisy and false values with mock dismay and worldly tolerance. He sprinkles the book with personal observations, some of which we could do without, but many of which are pointed and humorous. All and all, a wonderful novel, evocative of the mid-nineteenth century, timely as today's jet set. Recommended without qualification.

Lesser lights of nineteenth-century England

Other notable English novels of this period are *Wuthering Heights* by Emily Brontë (1818–1848), *Jane Eyre* by Charlotte Brontë (1816–1855), *Middlemarch, Adam Bede,* and *The Mill on the Floss* by George Eliot (1819–1880). The first two are tales of romance and mystery which have remained perennially popular. George Eliot's works are somber, realistic and heavily moralistic.

In the latter part of the nineteenth century the leading English novelist was Thomas Hardy (1840–1928), whose brooding novels have been compared with Greek tragedies in their preoccupation with an inexorable fate. They are now much less popular than they once were; *The Return of the Native* is one of those novels traditionally esteemed by English teachers and heartily disliked by students.

Other respected novelists of Victorian England were: George Meredith (1828–1909) whose satiric works, such as *The Egoist,* are written in some of the densest, most ornate prose to be found anywhere; Robert Louis Stevenson (1850–1894), whose *Treasure Island* and *Kidnapped* have entertained youngsters of several generations; Anthony Trollope (1815–1882), a keen social observer best remembered for *Barchester Towers;* and Oscar Wilde (1854–1900) whose *The Picture of Dorian Gray* remains popular. And let us not forget those gems of Lewis

Carroll (1832–1898): *Alice in Wonderland* and *Through the Looking-Glass.*

The French novel: Stendahl and Balzac

In France the novel came of age with those two giants of the early nineteenth century, Stendahl (1783–1842) and Honoré de Balzac (1799–1850). *The Red and the Black* by Stendahl recounts the rise and fall of Julian Sorel, an ambitious and opportunistic young man in post-Napoleonic France. This book has a distinctly modern flavor, compounded of irony and psychological insight, that makes the English novels of the period seem old-fashioned by comparison. Considered one of the great novels of all time, *The Red and the Black* has aged well. It qualifies for our list of required reading.

Balzac was an intense titan of a man who wrote more than one hundred novels, and whose plan embraced, in his words, "not only a history and criticism of society, but also an analysis of its evils and an exposition of its principles." No one of his novels achieved the status of a masterpiece, but taken together they constitute a powerful picture of the often desperate lives of ordinary men in money-dominated, bourgeois society. *Eugénie Grandet, Old Goriot,* and *Cousin Bette* are three of his more memorable works.

Flaubert and other French novelists to 1900

The art of the French novel reached what many consider to be its highest point in 1857 with the publication of *Madame Bovary* by Gustave Flaubert (1821–1880). Emma Bovary, having read and dreamed of romance, finds only monotony and disillusionment in life, first with her husband, then in illicit love affairs. She is crushed by the real world, the nature of which she so poorly understands. A carefully wrought book by a master stylist and a landmark in the development of the novel toward psychological realism, *Madame Bovary* is a work to be admired, not necessarily to be read by the twentieth-century engineer.

Other important novelists of nineteenth-century France are Alexandre Dumas (1802–1870), creator of *The Count of Monte Cristo* and *The Three Musketeers;* Victor Hugo (1802–1885), romantic poet, dramatist, and author of *The Hunchback of Notre Dame* and *Les Misérables;* Guy de Maupassant (1850–1893), best known for his short stories; Anatole France (1844–1924), the brilliant satirist; and Émile Zola (1840–1902), whose method of "scientific naturalism" produced powerful attacks against social injustice, but not very agreeable works of literature.

The Russian giants: Tolstoy and Dostoevsky

In the history of the novel, indeed in the history of all literature, 1866 must be accounted a memorable year. This is the year that saw the appearance of *War and Peace* and *Crime and Punishment,* two novels which rank with the very greatest literary creations.

War and Peace, by Leo Tolstoy (1828–1910), is an epic chronicle of Napoleon's invasion of Russia in 1812. Here is a masterful composition, spread on a gigantic canvas by a supreme artist. There is glitter and pageantry, nobility and high drama, love and tenderness—a most spectacular representation of everything that is glorious in life. Yet underlying all is a deep religious feeling, an awareness that men's most momentous deeds are as naught in the eyes of God, and an abiding belief that the stolid, unchanging life of the peasant is more meaningful than the strutting of the mighty. It is a very long book, to be sure, more than thirteen hundred pages, and is a little difficult to get into, what with all the Russian names and constant changes of scene. But this is one novel that is well worth whatever effort it requires of the reader.

Tolstoy's other great novel is *Anna Karenina*, with a theme of melancholy adultery reminiscent of *Madame Bovary*. An outstanding depiction of character and society, it pales, nevertheless, in comparison with *War and Peace*. For the reader who, for all his good intentions, simply cannot undertake the reading of *War and Peace*, Tolstoy's short story, *The Death of Ivan Ilyitch*, is recommended.

Crime and Punishment is one of the best of several superb novels by the other Russian genius, Fëdor Dostoevsky (1821–1881). Raskolnikov, an impoverished student, murders a dreadful old woman for reasons that he considers logically sound. Thus the stage is set for a fascinating detective story which is also an exploration of the deepest recesses of the tortured mind of the intellectual. Dostoevsky is obsessed with the contradictions within the human soul, the apparent addiction to suffering which goes hand in hand with the desire for comfort, and the compassion and saintliness which are found alongside lust and greed. His characters seek both guilt and redemption.

Where Tolstoy looks back toward a world of serenity and faith, Dostoevsky feverishly probes into a future of anguish and nothingness, and seeks salvation there. He is the true precursor of modern literature, and has been acknowledged as such by many twentieth-century writers. He put no stock in the communistic beliefs that were already current in his time and considered man's dilemma to be beyond any possible political solution. He anticipated many of the ideas of Freud, but would have scoffed at the idea of a medical remedy for man's torment.

Dostoevsky is even harder to read than Tolstoy, but his novels are more philosophically pertinent. *Crime and Punishment* and *The Brothers Karamazov* are considered his greatest novels, and one or the other should be known to each of us. "The Grand Inquisitor," a chapter from *The Brothers Karamazov* which stands on its own as a short story, is perhaps Dostoevsky's best-known piece of work. As a bare minimum put this on our "must" list.

Other Russians

The father of Russian prose is Nikolai Gogol (1809–1852), whose *Dead Souls* is considered a minor classic. The other famous Russian novelist is Ivan Turgenev (1818–1883). His *Fathers and Sons* is an early treatment of the themes of youthful rebellion and political nihilism, themes which have become increasingly significant in literature, as in life.

To the drama Russia has contributed Anton Pavlovich Chekhov (1860–1904), whose subdued and melancholy works remain a staple in repertory throughout the world.

The American Renaissance

During its early years, the young American nation had very little to be proud of in the way of *belles lettres*. There were the well-known stories of Washington Irving (1783–1859), to be sure, and the widely-read Leatherstocking Tales of James Fenimore Cooper (1789–1851). But these were minor achievements, and all else was mediocre at best. Suddenly in the mid-nineteenth century, there burst upon the scene six exceptional literary talents. Ralph Waldo Emerson (1803–1882) wrote essays which both reflected and helped to form the best qualities of the American character. Henry David Thoreau (1817–1862) wrote *Walden,* the beautiful book we all think of whenever conversation turns to the satisfactions of the simple life, close to nature. Edgar Allan Poe (1809–1849), America's foremost romantic, wrote fantastic tales and resonant poems. Walt Whitman (1819–

1892) exuberantly celebrated democracy, sex, and all of humanity in the thundering free verse of *Leaves of Grass*. Nathaniel Hawthorne (1804–1864) created novels that he chose to call "romances," chief among them *The Scarlet Letter*, a haunting tale of sin and guilt set in seventeenth-century Puritan New England. And finally, Herman Melville (1819–1891) wrote his richly symbolic tales of the sea, including the mighty *Moby Dick*.

Each of the six American artists just mentioned is well worth reading in depth. They are all recommended. But among their works the tale of the great white whale stands supreme, as indeed it does among all American novels. Captain Ahab is modern man—restless, brooding, challenging the universe. Moby Dick is Fate, or God, or Nature, or Evil, or Knowledge, or whatever our imagination tells us he is, as the gripping saga of the hunt lashes at our consciousness. This is a book to stand near the very top of our reading list.

Melville's *Billy Budd* is another allegorical novel with the sea as a setting. Good and evil and the meaning of justice will never seem the same again to the reader of this stunning short novel.

Mark Twain and Henry James

The brilliant renaissance of the mid-nineteenth century was followed by a decline in American letters. Until well after the Civil War, the novel was dominated by what Hawthorne called a "damned mob of scribbling women." Finally, in the last quarter of the century, the literary scene was brightened by the appearance of works by Mark Twain (1835–1910) and Henry James (1843–1916).

Twain's imagination and satiric wit reflected the spirit of the developing nation. *Huckleberry Finn*, once thought to be a book for boys, has come to be regarded as a true folk epic; Huck is naïve, well meaning and free-wheeling—the embodiment of a vibrant young democracy.

Henry James—born in America but a resident of Europe much of his life—is as different from the Missourian, Mark Twain, as one writer can be from another. Although James, too, contrasts American ingenuousness with Old World sophistication, he does it, not breezily, like Twain, but painstakingly, as part of a rich and complex picture of society. James is known for his delicate sense of the nuances of human behavior and for his careful recording of manners and of the growth or decay of moral consciousness in his central characters. That he paid so much attention to manners does not mean that his works are at all superficial. Manners were studied by James "as the indication of the direction of man's soul."[8] *Portrait of a Lady* and the novellettes *Daisy Miller* and *The Turn of the Screw* are among his well-known works.

Mark Twain and Henry James are two important and talented artists who played important roles in the development of the novel. Both are still enjoying excellent reputations and are popular with connoissieurs of good literature. Unfortunately, for today's average reader Twain is often too folksy and James is too subtle. James in particular offers rich rewards, but only to the reader who is willing to work.

Before the First World War

As the twentieth century dawned, the Western world was enjoying a period of relative tranquility. The wonders of science seemed to promise an increasingly pleasant future. The abyss of World War I was not yet in view.

In England, Rudyard Kipling (1865–1936) extolled the glory of the British Empire, then at its zenith. Samuel Butler (1835–1902) was considered quite daring when he registered a personal protest against parental authority and Victorian ways in his autobiographical *The Way of All Flesh*. George Bernard Shaw (1856–1950) wittily criticised the foibles of the time, but was confident that what he called the "life force" might eventually see mankind through to a brighter day. Arnold Bennett (1867–1931) and John Galsworthy (1867–1933) placidly described a society that was soon to be shaken down to its very roots. H. G. Wells (1866–1946) sounded the alarm, foreseeing with dread the potential consequences of the new technology; but his books aroused more curious interest than fear.

In France, Romain Rolland (1866–1944) started work on *Jean Christophe,* a giant of a novel about a vibrant, Beethoven-like composer, a book that throbs with romantic faith.

In the United States there were some signs of uneasiness brewing beneath a surface of optimism. Before the turn of the century William Dean Howells (1837–1920) had shown the way to a new social "realism," and Stephen Crane (1871–1900) had written a remarkable and shocking novel about war entitled *The Red Badge of Courage.* In 1900 Theodore Dreiser's (1871–1945) *Sister Carrie* appeared, a harsh book which looked behind the facade of an apparently contented society and found sordidness and despair. In 1901 Frank Norris (1870–1902) wrote *The Octopus,* a slashing attack against the tentacles of the railroad empires. *The Jungle,* by Upton Sinclair (1878–   ), appeared in 1906, appalled a nation, and resulted in reforms in the meat-packing industry.

But these books were exceptions to the prevailing atmosphere of satisfaction and confidence in the future. Most of the nation's readers thrilled to the adventure tales of Jack London (1876–1916), delighted in the ingenious short stories of O. Henry (1862–1910), enjoyed the genteel novels of Edith Wharton (1862–1937), and devoured the rags-to-riches sagas of Horatio Alger (1834–1899).

The very stability that makes the years before the first great war seem idyllic in retrospect appears to have had a restraining influence on literature. It is sobering to observe that the up-heavals and uncertainties of the years ahead would trigger more vital literary creativity than did this extended period of peace and security.

Two masters of the novel:
Conrad and Forster

Two English novelists who were quietly at work during these years more than compensate for any deficiencies of their con-temporaries. The novels of Joseph Conrad (1857–1924) and E. M. Forster (1879–   ) I recommend before almost all others to the readers of this book. Together they make, in my opinion, one of the best possible introductions to serious litera-ture for the would-be serious reader. Conrad and Forster are not discouragingly difficult, yet their styles are complex enough to exercise and delight the mind, and their views of life are rich in provocative ambiguity. They are modern men who foresaw clearly the psychological, social, and religious crises of the twen-tieth century. But they wrote at a time before total disaster had struck, and they were still able to feel—as so many modern artists cannot—that man *counts,* that life is *important.*

In most of Conrad's books we find men at the ends of the earth, in jungles or sailing the eastern seas, and in these exotic surroundings we probe into the depths of the human soul. What we find there is isolation, decay, and fear, but also redemption through moral courage. By means of vivid settings, exciting ad-ventures, and profound philosophical symbolism, Conrad ap-peals to our boyish love for the sea, to our sense of mystery, and to our moral intelligence. Meet him first in his short novels, *Heart of Darkness, The Nigger of the Narcissus,* and *The Secret Sharer;* and then, if he grips you as I think he will, proceed to one of his longer and more difficult books, *Lord Jim* or *Victory.*

With E. M. Forster we travel not to remote lands, but into

the delicate web of civilized society. His mood is buoyant, almost frivolous, compared with Conrad's somber brooding. Yet the quest is not so very different: with Forster as with Conrad we are in search of an understanding of human motives and needs and of an answer to the question of why most men fail to achieve fulfillment in life.

In *Howard's End* the family of Henry Wilcox, a successful businessman who lives in a world of "telegrams and anger," is contrasted with the two young Schlegel sisters, who are esthetes and intellectuals. At first the practical and masculine ways of the Wilcoxes make the values of the Schlegels appear inadequate by comparison. Eventually we see that sensitivity and an awareness of "invisible values" make life worth living, and that behind the solid, good sense of the Wilcoxes there is nothing but "panic and emptiness." This is not a simple-minded attack on the businessman (as are some of our more recent novels), but a perceptive and wise consideration of middle-class society, and of the quality of life in our time.

Howard's End is Forster's masterpiece, but each of his novels is a gem in its own way: *Where Angels Fear to Tread, The Longest Journey, A Room With a View,* and the famous *A Passage to India,* written in 1924 long after the others.

A philosophical thriller

Before we leave this period of the early 1900s, let me mention a personal favorite—a book that will not be found on any reading lists that I know of, but one that I recommend heartily. *The Man Who Was Thursday* by G. K. Chesterton (1874–1936), is an exciting mystery story, which gallops along at a great pace. Suddenly the reader finds that the quarry is more than a master criminal and that this is not a mere whodunit but rather an excitingly different sort of book that I can only call a philosophical thriller. Try it.

World War I was called by E. M. Forster "the sinister corridor of our age." Once having passed through this corridor, the world could never be the same again. Lost innocence and shattered dreams—these were the fruits of those grim years. The general sense of disillusionment was summed up in the expression, "the lost generation." To artists and intellectuals it appeared that the theories of Darwin, Marx, and Freud were being borne out by the savage, competitive, and irrational behavior of man. It no longer seemed possible to think of humanity in terms of the heroic, the divine, or even the reasonable. The institutions of men—the governments, the armies, the churches, the industrial empires, the class structures—these, of course, were completely discredited. Add to all this the oppressive influence of the rising crescendo of scientific discovery, including quantum theory and the theory of relativity, and the outlines of the modern mood of desolation become clear.

In 1921, William Butler Yeats (1865–1939), the great Irish poet, wrote

> Things fall apart; the centre cannot hold;
> Mere anarchy is loosed upon the world . . .

The following year the world shivered to "The Waste Land" of T. S. Eliot (1888–1965).

> We who were living are now dying
> With a little patience

In America Eugene O'Neill (1888–1953) wrote such harsh and doleful plays as *Anna Christie* and *Desire Under the Elms.* Sherwood Anderson (1876–1941), in *Winesburg, Ohio,* launched an angry attack against the values of small-town, middle-class life. In 1922 Sinclair Lewis (1885–1951) took up the same attack, but with flair and satiric wit; the result was *Babbitt*, a minor classic whose hero almost immediately became, and has remained, a symbol of all that is shallow and fatuous in the American businessman.

F. Scott Fitzgerald (1896–1940), with the publication of *The Great Gatsby* in 1925, aimed his arrows of irony at the upper class. He is the writer we think of when conversation turns to the bittersweet days of "the twenties." For all his sad decline and tragic end, he remains one of the most skillful American novelists. *The Great Gatsby* is a landmark that can be read with great pleasure.

Hemingway and Faulkner

In 1926 *The Sun Also Rises,* by Ernest Hemingway (1899–1961), was published. This is the novel which more than any other defined the melancholy mood of the lost generation. Hemingway's posture is not one of anger or of sophisticated cynicism, but rather of stoic toughness. Bravery, loyalty, and a manly lustiness are the distinctive traits of the heroes of most of his stories and novels. Hunting, fishing, bullfighting, drinking, love-making—these are the activities to which these heroes are drawn. Hemingway is much praised for his spare and lucid style, and is often criticized for an immature philosophical outlook. Immature or not, he is one of the two major American novelists of the twentieth century, a literary figure whom we cannot ignore. Let us put *The Sun Also Rises* on our "must" list, with his more recent *The Old Man and the Sea* as an alternate. Neither of these slim novels confronts the reader with difficulties. In simple but eloquent prose they express both the despair and the fortitude of modern man.

The other major American novelist of this century is William Faulkner (1897–1962). The rich, complex novels of this gifted writer deal mostly with the dissolution of the old South under the pressures of rapacious commercialism. In contrast with Hemingway's straightforward narration, Faulkner's approach is oblique and often obscure. He skips around in time and place and speaks from the point of view of one character after another, building up a richly-colored picture of events by implication and innuendo. The magnificent technique upon which his high reputation rests unfortunately isolates him from many readers. The quotient of pleasure and enlightenment divided by the effort involved is often too low in his case. First-time readers of Faulkner might try his short stories, especially "Old Man" and "The Bear."

Other noteworthy American writers of the twenties were Willa Cather (1873–1947), whom we have met in the previous chapter, and Ellen Glasgow (1874–1945), guardian of the "genteel" tradition. As the decade came to an end, Thomas Wolfe (1900–1938) exploded upon the literary scene. A verbose, self-absorbed romantic, he was very much in vogue for a time. Today his popularity is much diminished, and I think rightly so.

England after World War I

In England the post World War I period produced three outstanding literary figures: W. Somerset Maugham (1874–1966), Virginia Woolf (1882–1941), and D. H. Lawrence (1885–1930). Maugham was a master storyteller of no great profundity whose invariably interesting and well-wrought fiction made him a rich man. Virginia Woolf was a trailblazer, one of the first novelists to experiment with the "stream-of-consciousness" technique. Her sensitive exploration of the human psyche won her a minor but permanent place among the masters of the novel. *To the Lighthouse,* her most famous work, is enchanting.

Lawrence is best known for *Lady Chatterley's Lover,* a novel that a less-sophisticated age considered scandalous. We can now see Lawrence for what he truly was—a supremely moral artist who felt that industrialism was cutting man's ties to the natural world, shriveling his sexual instincts, and fragmenting his spirit. "What the blood feels, and believes, and says," he proclaimed, "is always true." His reputation as a prophet and as an important literary creator is now secure. His novel, *Sons and Lovers,* is included in most lists of significant modern novels. Yet it is not a book that I can recommend with any enthusiasm.

The five masters of modern literature

In spite of all the artistic energy and activity in the United States and England after World War I, and in spite of the considerable achievements of Hemingway, Faulkner, Woolf, and Lawrence, it remains a fact that no American or English writer is included among the five great novelists of "modern literature." These masters are Marcel Proust (1871–1922) and André Gide (1869–1951) of France, Thomas Mann (1875–1955) of Germany, Franz Kafka (1883–1924) of Czechoslovakia, and James Joyce (1882–1941), who was born in Ireland, but who was a resident of Switzerland and Paris for most of his life.

James Joyce and Ulysses

Joyce's *Ulysses,* published in 1922, is perhaps the most famous novel of modern times. It carries the reader through a day in the life of Leopold Bloom, a twentieth-century Everyman searching for meaning amid the buffeting of modern life. This vast work is comic, poignant, and tremendously moving. It is also exceedingly difficult to read, consisting mostly of obscure, poetic, stream-of-consciousness prose, and filled with complex mythical references and patterns. It can only be recommended to the reader who has an abundant supply of time, energy, and ambition. Joyce's earlier work, *A Portrait of the Artist as a Young Man,* is shorter and more straightforward, but is in no way an equivalent of the monumental *Ulysses.*

Remembrance of Things Past

The other towering achievement of twentieth century fiction is Proust's *Remembrance of Things Past.* I cannot seriously recommend to my fellow engineers that they read the seven volumes that make up this enormous novel. The detailed study of the crumbling French aristocracy of the early twentieth century is fascinating, and the characters, and the relationships between them, are superbly etched. Yet, as a whole, the subject matter is not of compelling interest to us today. What is of compelling interest is Proust's conception of reality, his understanding that we are different people at different moments depending on the memories and moods triggered within us by our surroundings, that truth in human affairs is not fixed, but is rather the elusive aggregate of the constantly shifting views of many personalities. Proust's psychological theory, which permeates his work, is finally expounded in the first part of Chapter 3 of the last volume, *The Past Recaptured.* These fifty or so pages, more philosophy, perhaps, than fiction, make for one of the most thrilling reading experiences I know of. It is a sin, no doubt, to recommend the theory separately from the main body of the novel, but I do so nevertheless. If the reader is then carried on deeper into this great work, so much the better.

Mann and Kafka

Thomas Mann wrote novels, stories, and essays touching on almost all aspects of modern life. The relationship of art to life is the central theme of his famous novelettes *Tonio Kröger* and

Death in Venice. In his longer novels he started with the study of German middle-class life in *Buddenbrooks,* went on to an analysis of European Man in *The Magic Mountain,* and finally, in *Joseph and His Brothers,* plunged into the bottomless past, pondering man's "origin, his essence, his goal." All of these works are recommended. However, there is a Germanic heaviness about Mann that sometimes makes for heavy going. Let us try one of his shorter works first, say *Tonio Kröger.* The serious reader will eventually find his way deeper into the works of this brilliant and profound artist.

In the previous chapter we spoke about Kafka and his search for salvation in the midst of the nightmarish nothingness of modern times. His work is unique, surrealistic, and hypnotic—frightening yet funny. Mann called him "a religious humorist." A student of the modern temper will want to read *The Trial.*

The moral immoralist: André Gide

This brings us to Gide, of all "the big five" the easiest and the most fun to read. Gide faced the emptiness and banality of modern life honestly and unflinchingly, and decided to seek meaning in self-absorbed experience and in the gratifications of the sentient moment. Yet his sensuality and his impulsiveness are not ends in themselves, but rather a means of achieving a mystical redemption, for Gide is a moral immoralist, a religious transgressor. "Moral tragedy—" he writes, "the tragedy, for instance, which gives such terrific meaning to the gospel text; if salt has lost its savor, wherewith shall it be salted?—that is the tragedy with which I am concerned." *The Counterfeiters* is Gide's most famous novel, a wonderful book, although it is more a series of digressions and ideas than a novel of action. But I recommend that the reader try first *Lafcadio's Adventures,* a comic, picaresque tale which features a startling, gratuitous murder.

The depression years

The economic depression of the 1930s confronted men with harsh and immediate problems which made the spiritual gropings of the writers of the twenties seem suddenly inconsequential. In the United States a new generation of writers stepped forward to protest against social injustice and to excoriate the industrial society which appeared to be creating a hell on earth. Leading figures in this movement were John Steinbeck (1902–), John Dos Passos (1896–), and James T. Farrell (1904–). Other novelists, such as John O'Hara (1905–) and J. P. Marquand (1893–1960), looked closely at the middle and upper classes and found them as impoverished in spirit as were their fellow citizens in body.

Most of the American novels of the thirties, for all their good intentions, make dreary reading today. The best of the lot, I think, is Steinbeck's *In Dubious Battle* (and not the better-known *The Grapes of Wrath*), a stirring account of a strike in the fruit-growing industry. Let us turn our attention toward it for its historical interest and for its passionate plea on behalf of justice and brotherhood.

As we look back at the depression years, we cannot help but be struck by the fact that compassion and worthy sentiments have so often resulted in uninspired literature. Frequently a writer's feeling for individual people seems to be weakened in proportion to the strength of his feeling for causes. Propaganda, however commendable, is not literature.

The novel and "the system"

As the economic collapse of the thirties prompted some novelists to examine critically the world of bourgeois capitalism,

it prompted others to scrutinize the rising political systems of
communism and fascism. In *Brave New World* Aldous Huxley
(1894–1963) foresaw civilization degenerating into a dehumanized, absolutist society. George Orwell (1903–1950) was later
to take up this theme, predicting the coming of "Big Brother" in
1984. In *Man's Fate* André Malraux (1895–   ) examined
the convulsive lives of men in the midst of revolution. Arthur
Koestler (1905–   ) dissected the horrors and incongruities of
Stalinism in his famous novel *Darkness at Noon*. Politics
seemed to have carved a niche for itself in the world of the
novel, a world previously the province of the individual personality. Life could be beautiful, it was thought, if only "the
system" could be set to rights. This dream had tantalized men
before.

The shattered dream

After World War II the dream was shattered, perhaps once
and for all. It quickly became apparent to most thinking men
that no "answer" was to be found in any particular political
system—not in the democracy that produced a discontented,
money-oriented bourgeoisie, and least of all in the communism
which once had appealed to so many intellectuals. The bar-
barities of the war years had tainted indelibly the ideal of the
perfectability of man. The atomic bomb brought into question
the very ability of humanity to survive. These disillusionments,
heaped on top of those which had been growing through the
early years of the century, created an atmosphere of complete
irreverence, of contempt for the discredited ideologies of the
past.

This mood first emanated from Paris, where Jean Paul Sartre
(1905–   ) and Albert Camus (1913–1960) were making
the world conscious of a philosophical view called *existentialism*. We will be talking about existentialism as a philosophy

in the next chapter. However, as a literary force it can best be seen in Camus's novels *The Stranger, The Plague,* and *The Fall.* Man face to face with the absurdity of the world—this is the theme that Camus explores. Responsibility and commitment in spite of, or rather *because* of, the apparent pointlessness of life—this is the path which he would have us follow. *The Stranger* is so slender a book that one hesitates to call it a novel. Let us read it for its timeliness, for its haunting evocation of mid-twentieth century man, adrift but defiant, in the midst of an indifferent universe.

The contemporary yea-sayers

Surprisingly, we may find that ultimate disenchantment with the world has generated not so much a literature of despair as quite the opposite, a literature of spirited yea-saying, youthful exuberance, and zany humor. Particularly in the United States it is as if the young writers have taken a look at this terrible world and rededicated themselves to an affirmation of life—wild, wonderful, and unpredictable *life.* For society and its institutions they have nothing but disdain. It is to the individual that they pledge allegiance—to the glories of the body and the mind and the spirit, to love and friendship, to action and energy. Perhaps, they imply, a world of free-wheeling nonconformists can regenerate itself, rising like a phoenix from the ashes of commercialism, materialism, atheism, and war.

The leading contemporary writers of America are great fun to read. Most of them are brilliant stylists, far superior to their more somber predecessors of the thirties. More important, their zest whets one's appetite for living.

Saul Bellow and life in our time

Saul Bellow (1915–   ) is preeminent at the moment, having received much critical acclaim for *Herzog,* as well as for his earlier novels, particularly *The Adventures of Augie March*. If we are looking for a writer to tune us in to the sad and wonderful quality of life in our time, Bellow is our man. I would like to suggest a reading of *Henderson the Rain King*. It is not, perhaps, his most admired novel, but it is a spirited caper, ideally suited to animate us, sedate engineers that we are. Henderson, a middle-aged millionaire, full of untapped energies and indefinite desires, runs off to Africa, where he has a series of fantastic adventures. There he finds himself spiritually refreshed—through a renewed sense of universal love, and a vague and mystical identification with the All. As the book ends Henderson is on his way home. The plane makes a stop in Newfoundland and he steps outside into the cold air. Out of happiness he begins to run. We leave him "leaping, leaping, pounding, and tingling over the pure white lining of the gray Arctic silence."

Malamud, Mailer, and further "left"

Bellow's position is not merely at the top, but also near the center of contemporary American letters. To his "left," moving toward impetuousness and disorder, we come to Bernard Malamud (1914–   ) whose distinctly Jewish protagonists chase after life in a wonderful fever. His most admired novels are *The Assistant* and his more recent *The Fixer*. My own favorite, which I endorse whole-heartedly, is *A New Life*.

Next to the left is Norman Mailer (1923–   ), an *enfant terrible* who shocks, annoys, and dazzles. He is a hipster who throws in the face of middle-class America a frenzied sexuality, an impudent affirmation of "experience," however scandalous. Yet his brilliant way with words, his nimble mind, and his undeniable moral intensity make him one of the most interesting of all our writers and, in spite of some fascinating failures, one of the most promising. His first novel, *The Naked and the Dead,* is as good a war novel as we have. Among his others I suggest *An American Dream,* a blasphemous, exciting, and ridiculous novel that will delight and disgust, but never bore, the reader.

Moving on in the same direction we come upon *Catch-22,* the zany antiwar book by Joseph Heller (1923–   ); *On the Road,* Jack Kerouac's (1922–   ) frenetic account of the "beat generation;" and finally the way-out "camp" of the hilarious, incredible *Candy* by Terry Southern and Mason Hoffenberg.

Salinger, Updike, and Cheever

To the "right" of Bellow, moving toward conservatism, we find J. D. Salinger (1919–   ), who achieved fame with his adroit depiction of modern adolescence in *The Catcher in the Rye,* and who is now groping for meaningful spiritual values in his series of stories about the Glass family. We also find John Updike (1932–   ), seeking deep meanings beneath the surface of ordinary everyday living. He is much praised for his sensitivity and brilliant prose technique, occasionally criticized for lack of robustness and for exhibitionist overwriting. His novel, *The Centaur,* is an impressive achievement.

In John Cheever (1912–   ) we reach a writer who seems at first to be more conventional in his approach to the novel than the writers we have just been discussing. *The Wapshot Chronicle* and *The Wapshot Scandal* tell about three generations of the Wapshots of St. Botolphs, Massachusetts. There is the expected decline from the vigorous and independent New Englanders of the past to their less robust descendents, who are uncertainly confronting a world of neon and chrome. But we soon find that Cheever is not a discontented "realist" or a sedate novelist of manners. Exuberance and lustiness burst forth in the doings of this vigorous clan, and Cheever, for all his disenchantment with our insipid society, is seen to be another champion of the indomitable human spirit. Both of the Wapshot books are enthusiastically recommended.

The literary right wing

Far off to the right we find the true conservatives, the defenders of the structure of society—those writers to whom responsibility and order are what count, to whom egocentricity and anarchy are the things to be most feared. James Gould Cozzens (1903–   ) has written a series of novels about men of substance: men like ourselves, who get up every morning, do their duty, and make the world tick. *Guard of Honor* and *By Love Possessed* are two of his best novels. Herman Wouk (1915–   ) in *The Caine Mutiny* preached a memorable lesson in respect for properly constituted authority. Cozzens and Wouk are members of an extreme right wing, popular enough with the general public, perhaps, but receiving little recognition in serious literary circles.

The individual versus society

The fact remains that the mainstream of contemporary American literature, indeed of most important twentieth-century literature, has been concerned with the individual's revolt against the standards of society, with his search for personal fulfillment in the face of a hostile or indifferent environment. As Lionel Trilling has written, the chief idea of modern literature is that "of surrendering oneself to experience without regard to self-interest or conventional morality, of escaping wholly from the societal bonds."[9]

This brings us back to a conclusion that we had to face in the last chapter: between the goals of the engineer and the con-

temporary writer there is a basic incompatibility. We can hope
that the difference will be lessened, and we have discussed some
of the ways in which literature may move toward a more mature
and sympathetic consideration of technology. But there is
an element of creative literature that must always be at odds
with us, in a dynamic tension—*and it is best that this should
be so.*

The boisterous, egocentric, passionate literary artist is a
dangerous fellow, and if the world ever took him literally chaos
would ensue. Yet without him to prod us, to warn us, to shock
us, to pry open our eyes and to stir our hearts, we would be in
danger of losing, bit by bit, our sense of what it means to be
human.

Recommended reading

A large part of this chapter has already been devoted to recommendations. The reader is now invited to draw up his own
reading list using these recommendations as a guide only to the
extent that they coincide with his own taste. We should stretch
our taste, to be sure, and give a well-recommended book every
chance to prove itself. But there are so many more wonderful
books than we can ever read in a lifetime that we need not suffer
too long with any one if it is not to our liking.

Without exception the books recommended are available in
paperback, some of them in many editions. An excellent aid in
selecting preferred translations, and in planning further reading
on almost any subject, is J. Sherwood Weber (ed.), *Good
Reading* (Mentor Books MT558).

For introduction to the earlier periods of literature, and for
browsing when reading of complete works is out of the question,
the Viking Portable Library is ideal: W. H. Auden (ed.), *The
Portable Greek Reader* (Viking, P39); Moses T. Finley (ed.),
The Portable Greek Historians (Viking, P65); Basil Davenport

(ed.), *The Portable Roman Reader* (Viking, P56); James Bruce Ross and Mary Martin McLaughlin (eds.), *The Portable Medieval Reader* (Viking, P46) and *The Portable Renaissance Reader* (Viking, P61); Hiram Haydn (ed.), *The Portable Elizabethan Reader* (Viking, P27); Crane Brinton (ed.), *The Portable Age of Reason Reader* (Viking, P63); Howard E. Hugo (ed.), *The Portable Romantic Reader* (Viking P64). Also useful is Robert O. Ballou (ed.), *The Portable World Bible* (Viking, P5).

Needless to say, there are dozens of writers on the contemporary scene who are very much worth reading. I have stressed those few Americans who in my opinion are most deserving of our attention at this time. Among the many other American novelists of note, all of whom merit our attention: Nelson Algren, James Baldwin, John Barth, Vance Bourjaily, Truman Capote, J. P. Donleavy, Ralph Ellison, Herbert Gold, John Hersey (see Chapter 4), James Jones, Henry Miller, Vladimir Nabokov, Flannery O'Connor, Katherine Anne Porter, Philip Roth, William Styron, Robert Penn Warren, Nathanael West, and Richard Wright. A few prominent contemporary English novelists: Elizabeth Bowen, John Braine, Anthony Burgess, Joyce Cary, Ivy Compton-Burnett, Lawrence Durrell, William Golding (see Chapter 4), Henry Green, Graham Greene, Doris Lessing, Anthony Powell, V. S. Pritchett, Alan Sillitoe, C. P. Snow (see Chapter 4), Muriel Spark, Evelyn Waugh, and Angus Wilson. And from the continent: Gunter Grass of Germany, Nikos Kazantzakis of Greece, François Mauriac of France, Boris Pasternak of Russia, and Ignazio Silone of Italy.

With the entire world in ferment, new literary movements are constantly afoot, and a work of genius, or at least a work of special pertinence, is liable to appear at any moment. While we are reading those works which have been tested by time, we should also be aware of what is happening in the present. This is best done by following the literary critics in such respected quarterlies as *Partisan Review, Hudson Review, Kenyon Review,* or *The American Scholar;* monthly magazines such as *The Atlantic* or *Harper's;* weekly magazines such as *The Saturday Review, The Nation, The New Republic, Time,* or *Newsweek;* newspapers such as *The New York Review of Books* or *The New York Times Book Review.* Each publication has its special weaknesses and prejudices, and the reader would do well not to rely too heavily on any single one.

In devoting our attention to the novel, we have let writers of the modern theater go practically unnoticed. We have mentioned, in passing, George Bernard Shaw, Anton Chekhov, and Eugene O'Neill, but not the father of the modern drama, Henrik Ibsen (1828–1906), nor the great playwrights of Dublin's Abbey Theatre, most notably J. M. Synge (1871–1909) and Sean O'Casey (1880–1964). We have neglected such outstanding contemporary American playwrights as Thornton Wilder, Arthur Miller, Tennessee Williams, and Edward Albee; such French notables as Jean Giraudoux and Jean Anouilh; and the current writers of the English stage, John Osborne, the original "angry young man," Harold Pinter, and Samuel Beckett, one of the founders of "the theater of the absurd." Through the efforts of these creative artists, among others, the theater is struggling to regain its place as a vigorous force in the intellectual life of our society.

The cinema, too, has been developing from a mere entertainment into a vital art form, worldwide in scope. As we seek out the best in literature, we should also be on the alert for opportunities to attend the best in theater and cinema. In the eighteenth century the novel overshadowed the theater, which previously had been a dominant art form. Perhaps the reverse is destined to occur in our time.

As for poetry, an excellent anthology is W. H. Auden and Norman Holmes Pearson (eds.), *Portable Poets of the English*

Language (Viking, P49 through P53). Others with various merits: Hubert Creekmore (ed.), *A Little Treasury of World Poetry* (Charles Scribner's Sons, 1955); Arthur Quiller-Couch (ed.), *The Oxford Book of English Verse* (Oxford University Press, 1940); F. O. Matthiessen (ed.), *The Oxford Book of American Verse* (Oxford University Press, 1950); Louis Untermeyer (ed.), *A Treasury of Great Poems* (Simon & Schuster 75020 and 75021); Selden Rodman (ed.), *100 Modern Poems* (Mentor Books MP359); M. E. Speare (ed.), *Pocket Book of Verse* (Washington Square Press, W241).

A superb anthology of drama, fiction, and poetry is Lionel Trilling's *The Experience of Literature* (Doubleday & Company, Inc., 1967). Subtitled *A Reader with Commentaries,* this 1,300 page volume is a treasurehouse of great literature and illuminating critical commentary.

CHAPTER SIX

The Bridge
to Philosophy:
The Truth
of Science

"Tell me of what sort a man is," a philosopher has said, "and I will tell you what philosophy he will choose."

Engineers, as a group, are the preoccupied sort of men who choose no particular philosophy at all, at least in a formal sense. We take the physical world pretty much as we find it, with no questions asked. If pressed to verbalize our intuitive aversion to philosophy, we echo Francis Bacon, that father of the scientific method, who proclaimed blandly three hundred years ago, "that

151

rule which is most effective in practice is also most true in theory." Whatever works best is most true.

Engineers and the scientific view

After pledging allegiance to science, we may be tempted to conclude that we have settled the matter of our philosophical orientation once and for all. But upon reflection it becomes evident that scientific truth raises many new questions for each one that it answers.

Paradoxically, in spite of our scientific training, we engineers do not understand science very well. We use science, and we study it with increasing concentration, but only for the practical aid that it affords. We believe in the "scientific method" because it has proved successful in solving problems. But there is little evidence that we have been paying any particular attention to the philosophical implications of "the scientific view," in spite of the fact that these implications have been causing convulsions throughout the intellectual community since the days of Galileo. If we are content to think of ourselves as members of the scientific culture, then it is high time that we started probing deeper into science, deep enough at least to get an inkling of its meanings as well as its uses, of its message as well as its methods.

A fantasy of concepts

If we seek to penetrate to the core of scientific truth, we should beware, according to scientists, of asking *what* the universe consists of. Rather, we should ask *how* it behaves. In a sense, they point out, it is what it does. But this admonition is not likely to satisfy us. As engineers we are used to thinking in terms of substances. If we persist in asking the question in our own terms, science reluctantly answers along the following lines.

The universe is a space-time continuum of varying curvature. Where the curvature "increases," it manifests itself as an energy field, the dense core of which we call "matter." When, in the laboratory, we examine this "matter," (this "curved space-time," this "series of events in curved space," this "dense core of an energy field,") we find that it seems to consist of molecules, the molecules in turn consisting of atoms, and the atoms composed of elementary particles. Some of these elementary particles have mass, and so are said to be material, whereas others are quantities of pure energy. Mass, we now know, can be converted into energy and vice versa. Also adding to the complicated and enigmatic picture is the fact that the existence and behavior of the elementary material particles is governed by waves of probability; indeed they have been shown to *be* waves as well as particles, just as waves of energy have been shown to be particles.

These wave particles, or "wavicles" as they have been referred to, absolutely defy the conceptual imagination. They are unpicturable. Yet how could they be otherwise? If we should ask, "What makes chlorine gas green?" we would not be satisfied with the answer that it consists of green atoms, for we would then have to ask why the atoms are green. But, once we learn that jumping electrons in the chlorine atom emit and absorb wave particles which act on our eyes causing us to "see" green, we cannot reasonably ask, "What color are these electrons?" And yet if they have no color (to say nothing of shape, texture, extension, etc.), how can we visualize them?

"Though intrinsically unpicturable and unimaginable," says N. R. Hanson, "these mathematically described particles can explain matter in the most powerful manner known to physics. Indeed, only when the quest for picturability ended was the essence of explanation within all natural philosophy laid bare."[1]

"A piece of matter is the name we give to a continuous string of events," comments Erwin Schrödinger. "Some philosophers of the past," he muses, "if the case could be put to them, would say that the modern atom consists of no stuff at all but is pure shape."[2] James Jeans concludes that "reality is better described as mental than as material."[3]

Thus is the world, seemingly so solid and sound, so amenable to analysis and so predictable, suddenly dissolved by modern science into a fantasy of concepts.

The dissolution of value

Yet unsubstantiality is not the only unexpected and unwelcome feature of the scientific view. The worst is yet to come. Given the basic matter-energy of astronomy and physics, say the scientists, we can show how the more complex elements and compounds of chemistry evolved, and from these the extraordinarily complicated aggregates of chemicals which we call living organisms, and from these the multitudes of higher animals culminating in man, and from groups of men the organized colonies that we call civilizations. Evolution is the key—evolution through natural selection, the Darwinian theory. It is all so exquisitely simple. An accidental change occurs in an organism's genes, and if that change manifests itself in characteristics helpful to the offspring's survival in the face of certain hostilities in the environment, it will have a very good chance of being preserved. In other words, nothing succeeds like success. The change, or mutation, always occurs accidentally—perhaps caused by a cosmic ray direct hit or a mishap during cell division—and only rarely does a beneficial effect result. But the numbers of organisms are so enormous, and the time scale involved is so vast, that, as one biologist has put it, "the improbable becomes the inevitable."[4]

This, then, is the ultimate truth of science. Not only is the universe unsubstantial, and at its core unpicturable, it is nothing more than the end-product of myriads of accidental electromagnetic happenings.

To the layman—and at this point we begin to realize that in

the deep waters of science we are most certainly laymen—
the consequences of this truth appear to be intolerable. If everything consists of "atoms and the void" (Democritus's phrase will
still serve, although our concepts are admittedly different from
his), then the most beautiful and fragrant blossom is essentially
no different from the most loathsome and putrid sewage. Deep
within both we find the same neutral essence. A maimed child,
a diseased wretch, a lovely woman, a corpse, a snow crystal, a
butterfly wing, a gold coin—these are merely more or less complex arrangements of identical atomic particles. Love, terror,
delight, agony—these are nothing more than different wave
patterns interacting in the complicated molecular colonies which
we call brain cells. A masterpiece by Rembrandt is a conglomeration of paint molecules; a performance of a Beethoven symphony
is a series of wavelike disturbances of air molecules; a Shake-
spearean drama is equally without universal meaning. The
arrangement of colors, tones, or words is a product of blind fate
and mathematical necessity. There is no good or evil, nobility
or meanness, courage or cowardice, beauty or squalor; in short,
there are no absolute values of any sort. Clearly, free will cannot
exist. Given the original energy structure of the universe, everything has been a logical and necessary consequence. Life on
earth has no purpose or value, and will disappear unmourned as
soon as the sun cools off or explodes.

Before this prospect we engineers cannot help but recoil in
horror. Our professional life rests squarely on an underlying
commitment to the value of human civilization, and our every
act is a strong, although perhaps unarticulated, reaffirmation of
meaning and purpose in the universe. If, in the face of the
cosmos, our most valiant efforts count for absolutely nothing,
then our life is reduced to the level of farce.

But, although our profession commits us to the affirmation of
human purpose, it also demands that we face facts squarely and
follow truth wherever it may lead. This makes our dilemma
particularly distressing. For we know that the truth of science

is cautious, cumulative, objective, and public. It seems evident that no dictate of the heart, no appeal of authority, no sense of beauty or vision of heaven can, under the cold, clear light of engineering analysis, compete with the experimental findings of the scientific community.

Attempts at circumventing the truth of science

The hope remains that there may be a way to circumvent the somber philosophical implications of science without disputing its factual findings. "Try as he will," says Edmund W. Sinnott, in his wistful little book, *The Biology of the Spirit*, "the man of science finds it hard to reconcile the orderly and impersonal determinism he sees in nature with the sense of freedom, personal significance, and spiritual values that is so deeply planted in his heart."

Some thinkers have sought refuge in *vitalism*, resolutely denying that the mysterious "life force" is amenable to scientific analysis. But this position has become less and less tenable since the first decade of this century, when the French philosopher, Henri Bergson, made *élan vital* a household phrase.

The next line of defense has been established in a theory identified with Alfred North Whitehead, which is known as *organicism*. This theory holds that biology is, in principle, irreducible to physics, that an organism is somehow *more* than the sum of its chemical parts. Such an approach has an appeal particularly to those of us whose scientific education skirts far around the boundary of biology, and to whom living creatures seem of a completely different order than inert matter. But scientists maintain that adherents to this view have simply been overwhelmed by the incredibly large numbers of particles which we encounter in even the simplest forms of life. After all, the human brain, which is itself a product of evolution, is not equipped to think in terms of large numbers. We can readily visualize three objects, even four, five, six, seven . . . , but as the number grows larger we falter and a feeling of inadequacy, even dizziness, overcomes us. How are we, then, to imagine the possible creations of an infinite number of atomic particles active over a period of several billion years? As J. A. V. Butler says,

> It is probable, that the smallest visible cell contains about a quarter of a million protein molecules of many kinds, and larger cells many more. Taking the average protein molecule as containing about 20,000 atoms, we see that the smallest independently living units contain something like five thousand million (5,000,000,000) atoms, united into molecules of great complexity and all the molecules organized into a single functioning whole.[5]

He goes on to point out that there are as many or more cells in the human body as there are atoms in a single cell.

And how are we to visualize the potentialities of the living organism in action? If we spend just five minutes watching an infant in his crib, we observe an infinite number of acts of learning, observing, and experimenting. It seems like an eternity to us, and must certainly seem like one to the infant also. When we consider that the child experiences tens of thousands of these eternities in his first year, we begin to get the faintest notion of the mathematics of living.

But bewilderment and awe do not attest to the existence of mysterious organic forces. "For the practicing biologist," remarks William S. Beck, "organicism means little and contributes less. Thousands of biological scientists the world over, whether explicitly or not, have rejected this outlook and are proceeding upon mechanistic suppositions."[6]

The uncertainty principle

Undaunted, the beseiged defenders of man's soul have thrown up the last barricades deep in the center of the new physics, seeking in the *uncertainty principle* an indication that the universal machine at its very heart is not mechanistic at all. Since, as they point out, we cannot determine the location and speed of any particular elementary particle—indeed our very act of observing affects the particle observed—how can we claim that such a particle's behavior is governed by law? Since we can predict the average behavior of many particles, but remain ignorant of what any particular one will do, perhaps the individual electron jumps when it "wants" to jump. "The old physics," says one relieved physicist, "showed us a universe which looked more like a prison than a dwelling-place. The new physics shows us a universe which looks as though it might conceivably form a suitable dwelling-place for free men, and not a mere shelter for brutes."[7]

Philosopher L. Susan Stebbing has commented that those scientists who try to get as much indeterminacy as possible "out of the miserably small amount" represented by the findings of the new physics are merely escaping absolute certainty to fall prey to equally onerous statistical probability.[8]

Max Planck does not even concede this; he is confident that "the quantum hypothesis will eventually find its exact expression in certain equations which will be a more exact formulation of the law of causality."[9] In other words, the indeterminacy is only temporary. To this, physicist-philosopher Arthur Eddington caustically rejoins: "Thus the causal law is to be found, not in the quantum theory as it is, but in what Planck believes that it will eventually become."[10]

But Hindu philosopher Nalim Kanta Brahma takes Planck's prediction much more seriously:

> If future experiments reveal to us that the indeterminism supposed to exist in the movements of the electron is really nonexistent, philosophy would find itself helpless to prove its position if it now accepts the argument of Professor Eddington.[11]

So one by one the barricades fall, and those who would have defended their old philosophies within the framework of the new science are trodden under foot. As engineers we can only observe these proceedings soberly, pondering their significance.

Mind and brain

But wait! One last desperate possibility comes to mind. Thoughts, desires, pains—*they* cannot be reduced to electromagnetic phenomena. Thoughts are thoughts, not wave impulses. The mind is in and around the brain but is not identical with it. You can affect the mind by drugging or cutting the brain. You can place an electrode against a part of the brain and electrically force memory of a forgotten episode into consciousness. But the consciousness itself is something more than the electric impulse which evokes it—or so it seems.

Ah! answer the scientists, you have found out our secret weakness at last. As Erwin Schrödinger has written, "The scientist subconsciously, almost inadvertently, simplifies his problem of understanding Nature by disregarding or cutting out of the picture to be constructed, himself, his own personality, the subject of cognizance."[12] Yes, confesses Sir Charles Sherrington,

> . . . though living is analyzable and describable by natural science, that associate of living, thought, escapes and remains refractory to natural science . . . .
> If as you say thoughts are an outcome of the brain we as students using the energy-concept know nothing of it; as followers of natural science we know nothing of any relation between thoughts and the brain, except as a gross correlation in time and space.[13]

However, warn the scientists, do not think that the "stickiness" of the mind-brain problem is an issue around which can be rallied a counterrevolutionary movement of the spirit. Even if conscious experience is an embarrassment to science, it is of no great consequence. For one thing, where consciousness does appear, it is recognized as having gradually evolved from those unconscious mental reflexes which everyone agrees *are* mechanical. At what precise moment and in which subhuman species could this phenomenon suddenly have achieved transcendent stature? And furthermore, says Bertrand Russell, speaking for the world of science, "I see nothing impossible in a universe devoid of experience. On the contrary, I think that experience is a very restricted and cosmically trivial aspect of a very tiny portion of the universe."[14]

How different science appears to us after we have tracked it to its lair, hypothesis by hypothesis. How ominous suddenly seems this erstwhile benefactor. How hard it is to grasp that benevolent science, after having freed the world from irrational superstition, and after having provided our profession with miraculous new tools for material progress, has then turned about and, with one blow, stripped life of all meaning and value.

The response of science

Scientists, needless to say, are reluctant to plead guilty to any such villainy. The search for truth, they point out, creates its own values. Typical is J. Bronowski's bold retort in *Science and Human Values*. "Independence and originality, dissent and freedom and tolerance: such are the first needs of science; and these are the values which, of itself, it demands and forms."[15]

In the same vein Bertrand Russell asserts that "those who forget good and evil and seek only to know the facts are more likely to achieve good than those who view the world through the distorting medium of their own desires."[16]

And there can be no denying that the life of science provides its own rich rewards. These have been described in placid but glowing terms by Albert Einstein:

Out yonder there was this huge world, which exists independently of us human beings and which stands before us like a great eternal riddle, at least partially accessible to our inspection and thinking. The contemplation of this world beckoned like a liberation, and I soon noticed that many a man whom I had learned to esteem and to admire had found inner freedom and security in devoted occupation with it.[17]

But such serene satisfactions are not enough for us engineers. We are "doers" rather than discoverers, and we are only content when we feel that our activities are truly constructive and worthwhile. Unfortunately, scientific truth deprives us of this assurance.

The attempt of pragmatism

In 1906 William James gave a now-famous series of lectures in which he addressed himself to the task of reconciling the "tough-minded" and the "tender-minded" views of life, the "tough-minded" view being essentially the scientific outlook which we have been discussing, and the "tender-minded" view being the old-fashioned belief in human destiny and purpose which the engineering profession so desperately needs to maintain. James suggested that his philosophy of *pragmatism* could bridge this gulf. "The pragmatic method," he explained,

> . . . is to try to interpret each notion by tracing its respective practical consequences. What difference would it practically make to anyone if this notion rather than that notion were true? If no practical difference whatever can be traced, then the alternatives mean practically the same thing, and all dispute is idle.[18]

But this approach resolved nothing. The tough-minded used the pragmatic argument to sweep away all metaphysical speculation as "meaningless," since it had no practical consequence, whereas the tender-minded could label as "true" any proposition at all as long as it had what they considered the very practical consequence of making them feel good. But while the pragmatic philosophy of William James was subjected to a good deal of ridicule, the term pragmatism—the basing of decisions upon practical consequences rather than on theoretical presuppositions —survived, and became particularly identified with the American technological outlook. The pragmatic approach is characterized by a free-wheeling distrust of dogma, and it has served our profession well. But if one believes that there are *facts* in this world which are independent of human experience, then pragmatism, as a formal philosophy, is obviously inadequate.

The disdain of existentialism

To the existentialist, the findings of science are not necessarily false—they are merely beside the point. The realities of human *existence,* he contends, will not submit to mere logic. Analysis is all very well if one is content to dabble on the surface of life; but passion, yearning and anguish have prior claims on our hearts and minds, and they *will not be denied*. Martin Buber voices typical existential disdain for science when he speaks of "those unapproachable events about whose essential definition physics always troubles itself in vain."[19]

Strictly speaking, existentialism is not a coherent philosophical discipline. The various scholars, sages, poets, and journalists who are known to the world as existentialists agree about precious little other than their preference for passion over reason. For example, Søren Kierkegaard (1813–1855), generally regarded as the founder of the modern existentialist "movement," declares that in the depths of human despair, "in fear and trembling," in the utter unreasonableness of life, he finds evidence of God. "In his failure," he proclaims, "the believer finds his triumph." On the other hand, Jean Paul Sartre and Albert Camus find only "the absurd" at the heart of things, and it is this very lack of transcendent meaning that prompts them to make the most of their humanity. On a sort of middle ground between atheism and belief in God are those existentialists, such as Karl Jaspers, who speak of an abstract and amorphous "Being" with which, they feel, it is crucial for humanity to maintain contact. "It is important," says Jaspers, "for the movement of thought, as far as it can, not to sink through the vacuum into the absolutely groundless, but rather to hold the thinker open for the encounter with Being . . . ."[20]

"Encounter with Being, indeed!" responds the scientific thinker. And what is the nature or the quality of this encounter? Does the philosopher sit in his study ruminating until he drifts into a trance? And does Being then seek him out and reveal itself to him?

Half a Socrates

Philosopher Walter Kaufmann has noted that one of the saddest features of our age is the rapidly widening dichotomy between the existentialist and the analytical philosopher. Each of these is only half a Socrates, he points out, and "if the feat of Socrates is really to be repeated . . . , there will have to be philosophers who think in the tension between analysis and existentialism."[21]

This is pretty much the same problem that Lewis Mumford is concerned about when he pleads for a "dynamic equilibrium" between art and technics. And what else, really, does C. P. Snow have in mind when he calls for a reconciliation between the "two cultures" of the liberal arts and science.

Swept now one way by our confidence in science and then another way by what is essentially an existential commitment to life, we engineers find ourselves, willy-nilly, right in the middle of this human drama. Is it possible that we can some day serve to reconcile the opposing forces of existentialism and analysis, the conflicting viewpoints of the humanities and science?

An unfinished book

For the present our dilemma remains unresolved. But we have accomplished much if we have come to recognize that a dilemma exists of which we had previously been unaware. We have accomplished much if we have discovered that philosophy is not an old and dusty book which we can complacently ignore, but rather a vast and unfinished book of which science is just one chapter, and not the final one at that.

Recommended reading

A good, readable introduction to the concepts of modern science is George Gamow, *One Two Three . . . Infinity* (Bantam Books NP19). Another deservedly popular work is Lincoln Barnett, *The Universe and Dr. Einstein* (Signet Science Library P2517).

An excellent introduction to the philosophy of science is Sir James Jeans, *Physics and Philosophy* (Ann Arbor Science Paperbacks 19), and this should be followed by L. Susan Stebbing's critique of Jeans and some of his fellows, *Philosophy and the Physicists* (Dover Publications). More current and comprehensive, but technical and rather heavy going in spots are Philipp Frank, *Philosophy of Science* (Spectrum Books S34) and N. R. Hanson, *Patterns of Discovery* (Cambridge University Press 261).

Three splendid books by outstanding men of science who are interested in the broad outlook are Sir Charles Sherrington, *Man on His Nature* (Mentor Books MT554); J. Z. Young, *Doubt and Certainty in Science* (Galaxy Books 34); and J. Robert Oppenheimer, *Science and the Common Understanding* (Simon & Schuster, 1954). If only there were engineers who could write like these scientists!

A brisk defense of the philosophy of science is J. Bronowski,

Science and Human Values (Torchbooks TB505). Perhaps the most unwavering and persuasive proponent of the scientific view is the great British philosopher, Bertrand Russell. Try his *Mysticism and Logic* (Anchor Books A104) and *Our Knowledge of the External World* (Mentor Books MP298). For a softer more reverent approach, turn to Alfred North Whitehead, a some-time associate of Russell's, whose historical-philosophical *Science and the Modern World* (Mentor Books MP538) is still a classic, in spite of some fuzzy sections on "organicism." Other interesting works which seek to uphold spiritual values in the face of modern scientific facts are Edmund W. Sinnott, *The Biology of the Spirit* (Compass Books C17) and Joseph Wood Krutch, *The Measure of Man* (Charter Books 103). Fascinating speculative essays fill the pages of Julian Huxley's *Man in the Modern World* (Mentor Books MP565) and *Knowledge, Morality and Destiny* (Mentor Books MP303).

An excellent review and anthology of twentieth-century philosophy is Morton White (ed.), *The Age of Analysis* (Mentor Books MT353). Included are selections by pragmatists Charles Sanders Pierce, William James, and John Dewey; advocates of scientific analysis Bertrand Russell, Rudolf Carnap, and Ludwig Wittgenstein; existentialist Jean Paul Sartre; pre-existentialist proponent of the "life force" Henri Bergson; as well as contributions from George Santayana, Alfred North Whitehead, and others.

For a closer look at pragmatism, nothing is more to be recommended than William James' *Pragmatism* (Meridian Books M16). James is a lucid and congenial writer, and the first chapter alone, "The Present Dilemma in Philosophy," is worth the price of the book.

An admirable introduction to existentialism is William Barrett, *Irrational Man* (Anchor Books A321). An excellent anthology is Walter Kaufmann, *Existentialism from Dostoevsky to Sartre* (Anchor Books A213). The final selection in this volume is "The Myth of Sisyphus" by Albert Camus. Very much worth reading is the entire slim book of essays by Camus which bears this name (Vintage Books V75). Camus has no standing as a formal philosopher, but I know of no writer who has stated more eloquently the predicament of man in the modern age.

For those readers who would like to sample some of the deep existential and theological thought of our time, the following are suggested: Karl Jaspers, *Reason and Existenz* (Noonday Press N117); Martin Buber, *Eclipse of God* (Torchbooks TB12); Paul Tillich, *The Courage to Be* (Yale University Press Y11). Although these three books are profound and far from easy reading, they are definitely intelligible, and none is unduly long.

Finally, for an enchanting survey of today's philosophic scene, which discusses not only analytic philosophy, pragmatism and existentialism, but also Freudianism, communism, and philosophies of the Orient, I suggest Abraham Kaplan, *The New World of Philosophy* (Vintage Books V235).

CHAPTER SEVEN

The World
of Philosophy

Philosophy, which means literally "the love of wisdom" once embraced all facets of intellectual life. Today, however, professional philosophers have an almost negligible effect on the intellectual climate of our age.

Once *truth* was sought in the branch of philosophy known as *logic*. Today, when we wish to increase our knowledge of the "truth," we turn to the scientist or the mathematician for guidance.

An understanding of *beauty* was pursued in the branch of

philosophy known as *esthetics*. Today artists and art critics define the beautiful, paying little heed to philosophers.

Goodness was sought in the branch of philosophy known as *ethics*. Today religious leaders, novelists and poets, social scientists, even journalists—just about everyone except professional philosophers—are looked to for the definition of right and wrong.

Ultimate principles and causes, the nature of reality, the essence of the universe—these were speculated about in the branch of philosophy known as *metaphysics*. Today metaphysics is a word very little heard except as an object of derision.

A curious fascination

Yet philosophy is something to which the thoughtful man cannot help but be drawn. There is, as William James has said, "a curious fascination in hearing deep things talked about . . . . We get the problematic thrill, we feel the presence of the vastness." Not only do "philosophy's results concern us all most vitally," says James, but "philosophy's queerest arguments tickle agreeably our sense of subtlety and ingenuity."[1]

In the last chapter we considered briefly the world views of modern science, pragmatism, and existentialism. But these are relatively new outlooks, in a sense united in their rejection of the aims of traditional philosophy. Modern science seeks to eliminate the human and subjective element in truth. Pragmatism and existentialism exalt the individual and deny the possibility of any purely objective truths. Philosophers of earlier times sought to formulate a meaningful world view incorporating both themselves and the natural world about them.

If we wish to know what, traditionally, philosophy has been all about, we must look back to a time when men knew less but meditated more—when the universe was an almost total mystery, but the philosopher was not ashamed to take his place in the center of it.

Entangled in epistemology

If we wish to spend time in the company of pre-twentieth-century philosophers we must accustom ourselves to grappling with problems which, in the light of present-day knowledge, hardly seem like problems at all. For example, if we seek from the traditional philosophers an answer to the question, "What is the nature of the universe?" they answer almost unanimously, "First we must determine *whether* men can hope to *know* the universe and, if so, *how* such knowledge is possible." Before we realize what has happened, we find ourselves entangled in disputes about the nature of knowledge. *Epistemology* is another way of saying "theory of knowledge," and epistemological dispute has had a strangle hold on philosophy for centuries. In vain have a few thinkers pointed out that *how* we know is only a small part of *what* we know. Most philosophers have insisted on starting with the *how*.

Rationalism and empiricism

On the question of how we gain knowledge, controversy has raged between the two camps of *rationalism* and *empiricism*.

The rationalists believe that the principal path to knowledge and truth is through thinking, that experience and observation alone are not a sufficient foundation for knowledge. They believe that the mind itself has an innate capacity to discover important truths without reference to experience and is, indeed, endowed with intuitive, *a priori* knowledge. In Spinoza's words, "the intellect, by its native strength . . . reaches the summit of wisdom."

The empiricists, on the other hand, believe in experience,

that is, sensory perception, as the foundation of all knowledge. According to the famous seventeenth-century empiricist John Locke, the mind is "white paper, void of all characters, without any ideas," until experience furnishes "the materials of reason and knowledge."

The modern reader quickly loses patience with this quibbling over the subjective and objective elements of knowledge. There can be no meaningful thought without reference to experience —that seems obvious—but neither can experience be intelligible unless it is perceived by a mind which is dynamically alive, sorting, filing, manipulating and coordinating sensation. Meaningful experience, in short, is a process of *interaction* between an organism and its environment. Impatience with the epistemological dispute is aptly expressed by Bertrand Russell. "My own belief," he says, "is that the problem is scientific not philosophical, or rather no longer philosophical."[2]

Yet for all our new anatomical and psychological knowledge, the rationalist-empiricist controversy remains with us. The age-old question of rationalism versus experience is reflected, for example, in the current disputes about heredity versus environment and instinct versus training. Essentially it is a question of how each of us is disposed to evaluate the relative importance and independence of man in contrast to the world around him.

Idealism and materialism

Let us set aside for the moment the question of how we gain knowledge, and ask once more, "What is the nature of the universe?" Again we find the great philosophers lined up in two enemy camps—*idealism* and *materialism*.

The idealists start with implicit faith in the reality of their ideas and very often end by denying the reality of "things" except as they may be part of a collection of ideas. The materialists start with confidence in the reality of "things," and very often end by denying the reality of ideas except as they may be defined as a collection of sensations.

Plato was the idealist *par excellence*, claiming that the world we perceive is merely an image, behind and beneath which the mind and the soul can discover the "real" reality of pure, unembodied *idea* and *form*. Democritus, in a phrase that we already have had occasion to quote, said that, as far as he could tell, the world and its creatures consist of nothing but "atoms and the void."

Four basic concepts

Rationalism—Faith in intellect
Empiricism—Faith in experience
Idealism—Belief in the reality of unembodied ideas
Materialism—Belief in the reality of material things

These four concepts are basic building blocks which appear in all of the notable philosophical systems. Let us see some of the ways in which they have been used.

As engineers we are inclined to be sympathetic with the empiricist's faith in experience, and at the same time we tend to think of ourselves as somewhat materialistic. But if we should come to the seemingly logical conclusion that all empiricists, because of their reliance on experience, become materialists, and that all rationalists, because of their faith in the power of thought, become idealists, we would be quite wrong.

The fascinating edifices of the rationalists

Rationalists, with nothing but their intuitions to account to, have created some fascinating edifices of imagination that combine features of both materialism and idealism.

Descartes (1596–1650) attempted to encompass both the immaterial and the material by dividing all things into mind and matter, two separate "substances" of completely different qualities. He thereby satisfied the rationalistic insistence on the supremacy of mind, but also made allowances for the machine-like world of matter which the science of his day was discovering. This theory is known as *dualism,* and it fit in nicely with Christian concepts of the separation of body and soul, matter and spirit. But when it came to explaining how pure mind and pure matter could interact, particularly within the human organism, Descartes could do no better than to invoke the power of God.

Descartes defined "substance," whether mind or matter, as something which "requires nothing but itself in order to exist." To the Dutch philosopher Baruch Spinoza (1632–1677) this was nothing more nor less than a definition of God. He saw mind and matter as two manifestations of the eternal, infinite, and omnipotent Diety. In contrast to the dualism of Descartes, Spinoza's *monism* was an attempt to reconcile idealism and materialism.

Spinoza's God is synonymous with Nature, and there is much in this world view which is still appealing to the modern scientifically oriented thinker. To Spinoza, everything that is or happens is a manifestation of God, all is predestined, and history is merely the imminent revelation of His divine plan. Free will, of course, can have no place in this conception of the universe.

Leibniz (1646–1716) rejected both dualism and monism in favor of what the philosophy textbooks call *pluralism.* He saw the universe as consisting of myriads of indivisible units, not physical atoms, but *monads,* units of force or energy or mind. These monads form a hierarchy, from the lowest, which comprise inanimate objects, through the living, the conscious, the rational, and the heavenly, culminating in the supreme monad, God. Leibniz's vision is abstruse enough to be more than a little forbidding to the casual student, and the perfect necessity of his God-created universe has made him vulnerable to the satire of hard-headed realists like Voltaire (who wrote *Candide* with Leibniz in mind). However, Leibniz was ahead of his era in insisting on the relativity of space and time; and his pluralistic conception of the universe has found favor with some modern-day philosophers.

Descartes, Spinoza, and Leibniz constitute a mighty triumvirate—the three great, imaginative rationalistic philosophers of the seventeenth century. Their poetic visions beckon the seeker after truth, but like mirages on the great plains seem to dissolve as he approaches, leaving his thirst unquenched. Their intuitive certainties melt under the glare of analysis and scepticism.

The empiricists' murky fog of idealism

The empiricists, on the other hand, starting out with a clear-eyed faith in experience, were determined not to be misled by any so-called intuitive, *a priori*, certainties. Nevertheless, they soon found themselves lost in a murky fog of idealism.

Locke (1632–1704) in considering what it is that we experience, concluded that we can not experience *real things* but only *appearances* or our *ideas* of things. We say that we observe "a table," but in truth experience no more than a shape, a color, a hardness, etc. We never experience the table itself. The real table is "the supposed and unknown support" of the *qualities* we sense. But then, asked Berkeley (1685–1753), what right have we to assume that this supposed and unknown substance really exists at all? A table cannot be said to exist at all except as a perception in a mind. Happily other minds are there to perceive things even when we do not; otherwise the world would vanish whenever we closed our eyes; and perceiving all is the mind of God. The world is *real* although it is *immaterial*.

Only one more step remained to be taken on the road to complete empiricist chaos, and this was taken by Berkeley's successor, Hume (1711–1776). Just as there is no *substance*, said Hume, there is also no *self*, and for the same reason: it is not the object of any possible sensory observation or experience. There is no "I" for any of us, merely a procession of mental events. We are deluged by a perpetual torrent of sensation in which we are unable to identify "substance" or "self." Nor can we say that there is any relationship of cause and effect, since, again, we experience only individual events, never any necessary connections between events. All that we can truly say is that one sensation follows another!

Kant seeks a solution

It was this bizarre dead-end that Immanuel Kant (1724–1804) sought to escape. Kant shared the empiricists' contempt for intuitive truths, and he agreed that we cannot know what we cannot experience. (As individuals we may be *morally* certain of such things as the existence of God, but we cannot be *logically* certain.) Yet he also shared the rationalists' conviction that the mind is much more than a blank sheet of paper. The mind might not possess innate wisdom, thought Kant, but it is endowed with *a priori* notions of space and time and *a priori* concepts of understanding (such as unity, reality, causality, etc.) which Kant called *categories,* and which enable the mind to organize raw sensation. As for idealism versus materialism, here also Kant sought a middle ground. All we are able to really experience, he acknowledged, is the appearances of things as they are organized by our mind. But even though we can never experience *things-in-themselves,* we have no right to conclude that things do not exist.

Kant's efforts to bring order out of chaos in philosophy were noble, and considering the undeveloped state of physics and psychology in his day, quite remarkable. At this point philosophy could have followed the path of sanity by seeking additional clues to the real nature of the human mind in the beginnings of psychological science, and additional clues to the real nature of the universe in the rapidly evolving physical sciences.

The phantom universals of Hegel

But after Kant, in spite of the strong scientific currents which were beginning to flow, philosophy fell under the spell of Hegel (1770–1831), a misfortune guaranteed to alienate every man rooted by nature or by occupation in the world of practical affairs. Even the briefest outline of Hegel's thought suffices to show why.

With Hegel one must start by discussing *universals* and *particulars*. The terms themselves are not too difficult to understand. Universals are qualities common to a group of particulars. For example, "redness" is a universal common to a particular red ball, a particular red chair, etc. "Squareness" is a universal common to a particular square box, a particular square table, etc. To have knowledge of universals is to possess concepts; an awareness of particulars is called perception. Simple enough, surely, at least until Hegel takes over. The universe, he tells us, consists, not of substance, not even of simple percepts as Berkeley taught, but of universals, which are "real" although they cannot be said to "exist." Individual objects, on the other hand, "exist" although they are not "real"; they are brought into being by the convergence of universals. A stone is made of such universals as "hardness," "roundness," etc. It follows that the entire universe is *thought* externalizing itself, *spirit* manifesting itself, the *absolute idea* becoming increasingly conscious and realizing its potentialities. This self-realization proceeds by means of the *dialectic*—thesis contradicted by antithesis and resolved in synthesis.

The engineer's mind, which may take in its stride the most complicated mathematical formula, is staggered by an encounter with the profundities—or absurdities—of Hegel. How can this universe of steel and concrete and water—or even of electricity —be composed of phantom universals, mere "concepts"? On the other hand, we have already seen how a reliance on simple perception leads to the even more barren idealism of Berkeley and Hume.

Let us stop at this point to ask how it was possible that these philosophers, all brilliant men, by the exercise of their supreme logical talents could have been led to such varied and contradictory conclusions? What methods of reasoning did they use, and where did they go astray?

Deductive reasoning

Upon pursuing this line of inquiry, we find that the philosophers we have been considering all relied on *deductive* reasoning.

The classic example of this method is the following: (1) Socrates is a man; (2) all men are mortal; therefore (3) Socrates is mortal. If (1) and (2) are true, it can be *deduced* that (3) is true also, and we know it is true because it is coherent with the true statements preceding it. At first glance this seems reasonable enough. One moves cautiously from one true statement to the next in accordance with the strict provisions of self-evident logic. Yes, but where does one's *first* truth come from? Well, answers the traditional philosopher, for a first premise one must rely on an intuitive certainty, of course. Ah, there's the rub. For, as we can readily see, one philosopher's intuitive certainty is not necessarily shared by another. Furthermore, what is a first premise but a hidden definition? If we say that all men are mortal, we are not so much stating a fact as giving one definition of the word "man" or of the word "mortal."

Inductive reasoning

As engineers, we are inherently suspicious of intuitive certainties. In our work we rely a great deal on *inductive* reasoning, which consists of observing certain regularities in our environment, formulating a hypothesis to explain the regularities, and then testing the hypothesis in systematic, controlled experiments. This is, in essence, the *scientific method*. As for truth, if our beliefs *correspond* with the facts, as determined by induction from experiment, then our beliefs are true. It is as simple as that.

The complexity of truth

But it is not so simple as that. It is all very well to observe the world, say some philosophers, but where are your hypotheses to come from except from the deep, intuitive sources of insight, what Galileo called "the natural light of reason?" And what are dazzling mathematical tricks but deductive reasoning in its purest form?

Furthermore, say philosophers of another school, what do you mean when you say that your beliefs "correspond" to facts? If a man is lost in the woods can he compare his *idea* of the way out with the *real way*? No, an idea is an idea and a path is a path; the one cannot "correspond" to the other. However, the man can *test* his idea in action and if it *works* then it can be termed true.

The complexity of what is so glibly called "truth" begins to dawn upon us. Even the simplest scientific truth entails empirical observation and induction, intuitive hypothesizing and deduction, and experimental verification.

These are a few of the main fields of inquiry with which philosophy concerned itself prior to the present era of the ascendancy of science.

However, philosophy, which we have been considering theme by theme, can also be approached chronologically, man by man. The great philosophers were not anonymous spokesmen for timeless points of view. On the contrary, they were real men who, out of the spirit of their age and with the intellectual tools at their command, sought to forge answers to the eternal questions. Let us briefly review the most notable philosophers of Western culture.

First come the Greeks who "asked all the great questions, and suggested most of the possible answers."[3]

The aim of Socrates (469?–?399 b.c.) was to clarify concepts and to arouse a love of truth. His method was to lead others, by means of skillful questioning, to realization that their assumptions were inadequately founded. He would then show the way to sounder knowledge, although he made no claims concerning the possession of ultimate truth. He equated knowledge with virtue and proclaimed ethical questions as the highest concern of man.

Socrates wrote nothing himself, but is known to us mainly through the writings of his pupil, Plato (427?–?347 b.c.). Just where Socrates leaves off and Plato takes over, putting his own thoughts in supposed quotations from his master, is difficult to ascertain. Essentially the two philosophers differ in that the main concern of Socrates was clear thinking and virtuous behavior, whereas Plato sought to achieve a complete metaphysical interpretation of the universe.

Plato was a mathematician and a lover of geometry, and his view of the universe was shaped by this predisposition. We have already spoken of his idealism. Just as there is an ideal, timeless figure known as a triangle (not just specific triangles), Plato reasoned that there were ideal tables, dogs, etc. (not just specific tables and dogs). This way of looking at things influenced Western thought for generations, and indeed still influences it today. The best known of Plato's works, which take the form of dramatic conversations between Socrates and his companions, are the *Republic,* in which he discusses the ideal government; *Symposium,* which deals with love and beauty; *Timaeus,* about the nature of the physical universe; *Apology,* telling of the defense made by Socrates before the court of Athens; and *Phaedo,* describing the noble death of Socrates.

Aristotle

Whereas Plato was a mathematician, preoccupied with ideal geometrical figures, eternal and static, Aristotle (384–322 B.C.) was a biologist, concerned with the phenomena of growth and development. Aristotle saw in the processes of biological change an "attraction" of all things toward an "end." Like Plato's idealism, Aristotle's concept of growth as a sort of "yearning" molded Western thought, and proved to be a formidable obstacle to the development of science.

Aristotle's greatest contribution to philosophy was to define and classify the various branches of knowledge. He wrote the first textbooks in logic, known collectively as the *Organon.* His other great works were *Rhetoric, Poetics, History of Animals, Metaphysics, De Anima* (on psychology), *Ethics, Politics,* and *Constitution of Athens.* Like Socrates and Plato, Aristotle identified virtue with reason, and counseled moderation as a way of life.

Epicureans, Stoics, and Sceptics

Epicurus (342?–?270 B.C.) and the Epicureans saw things quite differently. For them philosophy and knowledge had no intrinsic value except when practically useful. Pleasure and pain were the criteria of rightness and wrongness, and the goal of life was happiness, or at least freedom from pain. Embracing the atomic theory of Democritus (460?–?370 B.C.), they saw the universe in mechanistic terms.

Zeno (335?–?265 B.C.) and the Stoics held a pantheistic belief in a Divine Reason which pervaded the universe. Their ideal was to live in harmony with nature and by rational self-control to achieve contentment.

Pyrrho (365?–?275 B.C.), Carneades (214?–129 B.C.), and the other Sceptics felt that there is no reliable criterion by which truth can be established, and they counseled suspending judgement, curtailing curiosity, and moderating the passions. In regarding peace of mind as the highest good attainable, the Sceptics allied themselves with the Epicureans and the Stoics. It should be noted that these schools of philosophy flourished during the tumultuous days when Greek power was in decline.

The Romans borrowed their philosophy from the Greeks. Lucretius (96?–?55 B.C.) was an Epicurean; Epictetus the slave (60?–?117 A.D.) and Marcus Aurelius the emperor (121–180 A.D.) were Stoics; Plotinus (205?–270 A.D.) was a Neo-Platonist.

Medieval philosophy

After the fall of Rome the philosophy of antiquity was almost totally lost from view. When it reappeared it was as an adjunct of Christian doctrine. The philosophy of the Middle Ages is known, with good reason, as "the handmaid of theology."

The eleventh and twelfth centuries saw the founding of universities in Paris, Bologna, Salerno, Oxford, and Cambridge. The teachers of philosophy and theology at these great institutions are known as the Scholastics. The philosophy of Scholasticism was developed by such famous thinkers as Duns Scotus (1270?–1308), Peter Lombard (1100–1160), Abelard (1079–1142), Anselm (1033–1109), and, above all, the great Thomas Aquinas (1225–1274).

The essential difference between Scholastic philosophy and the philosophy of Greece is that the Scholastics emphasized the "good," whereas the Greeks stressed the "true." Socrates, Plato, and Aristotle had declared that knowledge led to virtue, that truth was the supreme objective. To the philosophers of the Middle Ages the "good" was nothing else than the divine law of God, and virtue depended not upon rational conduct, but upon obedience to divine command as revealed in Holy Scripture. They sought, sometimes by very complex reasoning, to accommodate Aristotelian philosophy to the dogma of the church.

The rebirth of philosophy

Scholasticism eventually fell before the onslaught of the Renaissance and the Age of Reason. Francis Bacon (1561–1626) described himself as the herald of modern thought. In his *Novum Organum* he spoke out in behalf of the experimental method and inductive logic.

The founder of the "new philosophy" is generally considered to be, not Bacon, but René Descartes (1596–1650), whose dualistic rationalism we have already discussed. Whereas Bacon championed scientific experimentation, Descartes proposed to apply pure mathematical methods of reasoning to philosophy. "I think, therefore I am" is his famous starting point. His reasoning was strictly logical, but his reliance on intuition made him much less "scientific" than he claimed to be. The other two famous rationalists of this period, whom we have mentioned previously, were Baruch Spinoza (1632–1677) and G. W. Leibniz (1646–1716).

In England a protest against rationalism developed, as we have seen, in the empiricism of John Locke (1632–1704), George Berkeley (1685–1753), and David Hume (1711–1776). We have also discussed the valiant effort toward synthesis made by the great Immanuel Kant (1724–1804), and the mystifying detour into idealism by G. W. F. Hegel (1770–1831).

Reason and Romanticism

It should be noted that from Descartes to Kant we are in the Age of Reason, whereas with Hegel we have entered the era of Romanticism. Philosophers, as well as artists, cannot help but be influenced by the spirit of their age.

Two other significant philosophers of the Age of Reason were Thomas Hobbes (1588–1679), an extreme materialist who said confidently, "all that exists is matter, all that occurs is motion," and the noted mathematician, Blaise Pascal (1623–1662), who, in a contrasting mood, remarked plaintively that "the heart has its reasons that reason cannot know."

A leading philosopher of the Romantic Age was Arthur Schopenhauer (1788–1860), who proclaimed the primacy of the insatiable Will and the hopelessness of ever finding contentment in life. This was also the time of Søren A. Kierkegaard (1813–1855), the precursor of modern existentialism. By way of contrast, at about the same time Auguste Comte (1798–1857) originated *positivism,* a renunciation of all metaphysical speculation in favor of scientific classification of observable phenomena. An admirer of Comte was John Stuart Mill (1806–1873), who is remembered less for his philosophical acumen than for the ringing liberal sentiments of his famous essay, *On Liberty.*

The last half of the nineteenth century is marked by the appearance of the evolutionary theory of Charles Darwin (1809–1882). The philosopher Herbert Spencer (1820–1903) was an ardent apostle of Darwin's theory, and it is to Spencer, not to Darwin, that we owe the famous slogan, "survival of the fittest."

Nietzsche and the death of God

Perhaps the most celebrated philosopher of the late nineteenth century is Friedrich Nietzsche (1844–1900). This brilliant, tortured, iconoclastic, perceptive, shocking (and, in his final years, insane) genius made little significant contribution to the technical side of philosophy. But he drew together in his violent works the main currents of his age—Romanticism, revolutionary boldness, evolutionary bravado. And he foreshadowed the coming of twentieth century existentialism, relativism, nihilism, anarchy, and Freudian psychology.

"God is dead," he announced; *"We have killed him*—you and I." But Nietzsche was not disheartened by the "infinite nothing . . . , the breath of empty space." On the contrary, he was exhilarated. He preached the need to sweep away completely the old beliefs and inhibitions, and heralded the coming of "supermen," lusty, strong, and unfettered. He damned the masses for their conformity, for lazily, timidly seeking after comfort; he exalted the dangerous, independent, and heroic life.

Before and during World War II, Nietzsche was much condemned as a precursor of Naziism, but this charge is patently unfair. He despised democratic liberalism, but would never have condoned bestiality.

From Socrates to Nietzsche

With Nietzsche we have reached the beginning of the twentieth century, the era of scientific analysis, pragmatism, and existentialism—subjects discussed in the previous chapter. It is fitting that we have concluded this brief historical survey with Nietzsche, as it is that we began it with Socrates. Both of these great philosophers were more interested in the conduct of life than in the niceties of pure logic. Between their lifetimes lie the great ages of philosophy. Before Socrates, dogma and superstition dominated the thoughts of men; shortly after Nietzsche the reign of science truly began.

It cannot be denied that prescientific philosophy did not produce much in the way of useful "results." By way of contrast, as Bertrand Russell has said,

> Science has presented us with a new world, new concepts and new methods, not known in earlier times, but proved by experience to be fruitful where the older concepts and methods proved barren.[4]

Nevertheless, the great philosophers of the past retain their aura of splendor, and continue to merit the esteem of all civilized men. In many cases their speculations are admired today as works of art rather than as contributions to factual knowledge. Strangely this change in emphasis has done little to diminish their stature. They stand as a symbol of man's great intellectual and spiritual aspirations, and also as a reminder of man's limited capacity to comprehend the universe. In spite of their obscure ways and their monumental failures they inspire us to look occasionally beyond our mundane world of things, to broaden our conception of what constitutes truth and reality, and to let our minds wander unfettered in contemplation of the cosmos.

Recommended reading

In general, we should be wary of relying too much on abridgements and anthologies. But they do have their uses, and as an introduction to philosophy they are indispensable. If we go out blindly and attempt to read our way through one of the works of Spinoza, Kant, or one of the other great philosophers, we will very likely become bogged down and soon disheartened. But a guided tour, combining commentary with actual selections from philosophical literature, enables us to enjoy, and to a great extent to comprehend, this fascinating aspect of human creative genius.

Ideal for this purpose is the six-volume series, *The Great Ages of Western Philosophy* (Houghton Mifflin, 1957) issued in paperback as *The Mentor Philosophers*. The last volume of this series, *The Age of Analysis,* was recommended at the conclusion of the previous chapter. The first volume, Anne Fremantle (ed.), *The Age of Belief* (Mentor Books MT463) is recommended only for those genuinely interested in sampling medieval philosophy. But the intervening volumes are unreservedly recommended. Volume II, Giorgio de Santillana (ed.), *The Age of Adventure* (Mentor Books MT437) contains selections by great thinkers of the Renaissance, including Leonardo da Vinci, Thomas More, Machiavelli, Erasmus, Luther, Copernicus, Montaigne, and Galileo. Volume III, Stuart Hampshire (ed.), *The Age of Reason* (Mentor Books MT367), features Bacon, Hobbes, Descartes, Pascal, Spinoza, and Leibniz. Volume IV, Isaiah Berlin (ed.), *The Age of Enlightenment* (Mentor Books MT473), concentrates on the English empiricists, Locke, Berkeley, and Hume, with short contributions by several less prominent philosophers of the time. Volume V, Henry D. Aiken (ed.), *The Age of Ideology* (Mentor Books MT421) covers the greats of the nineteenth century, including Kant, Hegel, Schopenhauer, Comte, Mill, Spencer, Marx, and Nietzsche, among others.

Another excellent multivolume anthology is Saxe Commins and Robert N. Linscott (eds.), *The World's Great Thinkers* (Random House, 1947; Washington Square Press Paperback W962 through W965). This collection is not arranged chronologically, but rather according to theme. The four volumes are entitled: I, *Man and Spirit: The Speculative Philosophers;* II, *Man and Man: The Social Philosophers;* III, *Man and the State: The Political Philosophers;* and IV, *Man and the Universe: The Philosophers of Science.* Expository text is minimal, but the selections themselves are more generous than in *The Mentor Philosophers.* Also, this work contains representative contributions from the philosophers of antiquity, whereas the Mentor series starts with the Middle Ages.

The philosophers of antiquity confront us with a real problem. They occupy an extraordinarily important place in the cultural heritage of the western world. Yet there is no denying that they are not everyone's cup of tea. Indeed, much Western thought and art has developed in protest against the works of Plato and Aristotle. A sampling of Plato's dialogues is a must. Whatever they may lack as philosophy, most of them are literary masterpieces. Volume II of *The World's Great Thinkers* contains *Apology, Crito* and two books from *The Republic. The Portable Greek Reader* (see Chapter 5) contains selections from *Phaedo, Symposium* and *Laws* as well as the entire *Timaeus.* This is enough to give one the flavor of Plato, and his master, Socrates. The final part of *Phaedo,* telling of the death of Socrates, is required reading for all civilized men.

Aristotle is quite another story, formidable and forbidding. His science and metaphysics are next to impossible. Only in his ethics does he speak in terms that are meaningful to the modern layman. Volume II of *The World's Great Thinkers* contains five of the ten books of his *Nichomachean Ethics. The Portable Greek Reader* includes brief selections from several of his works.

Epicurus, Epictetus, Lucretius, and, particularly, Marcus Aurelius, are very much worth encountering, and they are adequately represented, for purposes of introduction, in Volumes II and IV of *The World's Great Thinkers.*

For those who would rather read "about" philosophy than

"in" it, there are many comprehensive surveys from which to choose. Popular historical reviews are Will Durant, *The Story of Philosophy* (Washington Square Press W916), and Bertrand Russell, *History of Western Philosophy* (Simon & Schuster 31410); also by Bertrand Russell, relatively brief and illustrated, *Wisdom of the West* (Premier Books M211). Russell is opinionated and controversial, but I think that his acerbic approach will appeal to the average engineer. The most lucid general text I have found on the subject is John Herman Randall, Jr. and Justus Buchler, *Philosophy: An Introduction* (Barnes & Noble COS41).

CHAPTER EIGHT

The Bridge
to the Fine Arts:
Utility and Beauty

The engineer designs and executes objects of utility. The artist designs and executes objects of beauty.

Utility and beauty—two very different concepts, and yet in some ways not quite so different as they might appear to be at first glance. For there is much beauty in many objects of utility, and there is some utility in all objects of beauty.

The beauty of utility

That there is beauty in utility is clear when we consider that our esthetic taste is determined by a biological and cultural heritage and that this heritage, being a product of evolution, has been shaped in great measure by the criterion of survival. Instinctively we are esthetically pleased by things which have helped our species to survive, things that have made us comfortable and secure: the snug house, the fire on the hearth, the field of ripe grain, the peaceful harbor at sunset. And we characterize as ugly most things that are uncomfortable, unpleasant, or dangerous: a swamp, a pile of refuse, a festering sore, the charred ruins of trees after a forest fire. It would be foolhardy for the engineer to try to prove, in the face of many venerable theories of art, that utility is the sole criterion of beauty, or of meaning, which is the other ingredient of art. But there can be no denying that our taste in art is influenced in great measure by what is, and has been, considered by the human race to be useful. This is one reason that our tastes are continually changing. Modern furniture, after proving its practical worth, soon becomes esthetically acceptable. The steam locomotive, once considered a grotesque monster, is now regarded as picturesque if not actually pretty. One wonders what eyesores of today will become the art objects of tomorrow.

Functionalism

There is a formal theory of esthetics which places utility squarely in the middle of its definition of beauty, but this "utility" is meant in an absolute sense, and is not dependent on the human evolutionary experience. Beauty, according to this theory, is simply "the promise of function," and examples of beautiful form created by and for function, such as the gull's wing, are cited from nature. This theory goes by the name of *functionalism,* and its adherents cherish such examples of human design as the American axe and the clipper ship, which seem to embody their functions in their unadorned forms. Purity and simplicity are the hallmarks of functionalism, and to the extent that we engineers avoid unessentials and embellishments, we may find our creations admired as works of art.

But much as we are gratified to find our quest for efficiency defined as a quest for beauty, we realize that some forms can never be deemed beautiful by men, no matter how pure and functional these forms may be. True, there is a certain esthetic pleasure which we derive from the things in nature that seem *ordered*—the snowflake, the crystal, even the atom. But life is more than geometry. Human attitudes and prejudices intrude, and the link between purity and beauty becomes shrouded in a cloud of ambiguity. The vulture's beak and the anteater's snout are both fine examples of pure functionalism and yet we do not find them beautiful. Similarly there may be activities for which the engineer must design—sewage disposal, oil refining, and others—which can probably never result in forms that men will consider beautiful. Further, there may be areas of design, particularly in the field of architecture, where geometrical purity and a haughty disregard for human sensibilities may result in forms so severe and barren as to be incapable of evoking a meaningful esthetic response.

The utility of beauty

Having discussed briefly the beauty of utility, let us consider for a moment the utility of beauty. It is, in a way, self-evident that beauty is useful. Any work of art that can make us happy, or relaxed, or enthusiastic can be said to be useful, in a medical sense at the very least; and a work of art that enlightens or inspires can be extremely useful politically and economically. Great works of art have served to give societies identity, goals, or patriotic fervor. And we are just beginning to learn a little about the ways in which color, light, and form can affect the productivity of workers and the pride and cooperativeness of ordinary citizens.

Yet, even when we consider all the ways in which utility and beauty are intertwined, we still cannot overcome our natural tendency to think of them more in terms of contrast than likeness. Indeed, contrast is too mild a word; the relationship between engineer and artist appears at times to have degenerated into something little short of conflict. At least many an artist appears to regard the engineer as an ogre assaulting the citadel of beauty which protects the sanctity of the human soul. "The triumphal march of the practical sciences has crowded out the magic of life," complains Walter Gropius in an article entitled "The Curse of Conformity,"[1] and his lament is echoed by artists whenever they write or speak.

The handicraft tradition

It was not always so. In earlier times the engineer and the artist were united in the person of the artisan, and art and technology were combined in the activity of handicrafts. Lewis Mumford has spoken of those seemingly idyllic days in glowing tones:

> In pots and woven cloths, in houses and shrines and tombstones, in churches and palaces, the worker contrived not merely to do the job that must be done, but to identify himself, to individualize himself, to express himself, to leave behind a message, sealed as it were in the bottle of art, for the pleasure and enlightenment of other men.[2]

It is evident that something precious is lost whenever mass production replaces the individual skilled craftsman. But men would be reluctant, surely, to forego the benefits of the industrial and scientific revolutions, benefits which might seem a mixed blessing to the artisan and to the connoisseur, but which are an absolute godsend to the masses who have been chained to the soil for centuries with little more opportunity than the beasts of the field to create or to appreciate art.

Moreover, the handicraft tradition has never really been destroyed, even in the most advanced industrial societies. For one thing there is a fascination, a creativeness, and even a *beauty* in working with machines which cannot be disregarded. We have not yet reached the point where machine operators do nothing else but push buttons and pull levers. They assemble and regulate and control and repair. Their work requires both knowledge and technique, and very often the quality of the manufactured product is determined in great measure by the degree of their skill. An oil-spattered mechanism may not seem as attractive to the fastidious as a piece of wood; yet it can evoke in the worker an intellectual and sensual response not inferior to that evoked in a cabinetmaker by a hickory limb.

Even where automation has advanced to the point where the worker's role is mostly routine, craftsmanship has not disappeared. We find it being reborn in the form of a hobby craze and in a resurgence of "do-it-yourself" projects. Technology has contributed to these new phenomena by creating a climate of interest in how things work, and also by providing the spare time in which men can follow up this interest. Perhaps the cementing together of plastic models cannot be classified as art; but often one hobby leads to another, one skill develops into a more demanding and creative skill, and eventually what was mere whiling away of time blossoms into art. If this seems like wishful thinking, just listen to no less an authority than Bernard Berenson:

> Already, in almost every civilized country, hobbies are rife among individuals with a certain leisure. As leisure increases, these hobbies will find more opportunities for spreading out and flowering into something more artistic, more creative, at once more penetrating and more expansive, pushing further and further back the flaming frontiers of the human universe and turning aspiring man into a hopeful rival of the Demiurge.[3]

Be this as it may, the artist's quarrel with the engineer encompasses more than the plight of handicrafts in an industrialized age. The artist sees his culture flooded with the products of technology, most of which he considers to be overstandardized, dehumanized, and downright ugly. And behind this deluge of tastelessness he sees the pervasive presence of the engineer.

In the field of machine design there is not much that we engineers can do to mollify the artist. Where machines can perform a useful service, we will design them, and if people want these machines—whether automatic can openers, shoe shiners, or whatnots—the machines will be produced. Some of these machines, perhaps most, will turn out to be unattractive —in spite of what has been said about the beauty of utility. And since attempts to transform machines into works of art by adding decals or chrome trim or the like have been highly unsuccessful, it would seem that our best course is to fall back on the stark simplicity of strictly functional design. In doing this we are at worst making ugliness as inconspicuous as possible, and at best we are achieving that purity which the school of functionalism considers true beauty. Lewis Mumford has spoken eloquently on this topic:

> The canons of machine art are precision, economy, slickness, severity, restriction to the essential, and whenever these canons are violated . . . the result is not the humanization of the machine but its debasement.
>
> Any effort to leave the human imprint, can only give impurity to the form and defeat the final result . . . . Perhaps the best effect of machine art is to make us conscious of the play of the human personality in the small area where it remains free, a differentiation so delicate, so subtle, that a coarse eye would hardly take it in and an insensitive spirit would not know what it meant.[4]

Of course the engineer is not free to design all machines as he sees fit. Those machines which are for consumer use pass through what Mumford calls the "perversion" of industrial design. And if the industrial designers and the market researchers and the merchants see fit to clutter up our basic designs with "styling" or decoration, there is not too much that we can do about it.

That we engineers should throw our weight onto the side of functionalism in machine design does appear desirable, particularly at a time in which we seem to be about to drown in an ocean of useless chrome excrescences. But we should also beware of adopting a needlessly rigid and restrictive set of design principles, at least where the general consumer is involved. If a housewife enjoys having the control panel of her washing machine look like the control panel of a rocket ship, perhaps she should be humored in this caprice. A little bit of whimsy never hurt anybody.

The very standardization that has made possible the remarkable achievements of mass production has also subjected society to the blight of monotony, and whenever we deliberately choose variety instead of sameness we strike a blow for the human spirit. Even the finest design, if it is reproduced often enough, first loses its attractiveness and then begins to grate on one's nerves. Between inefficiency, vulgarity, and conspicuous waste on the one hand, and regimentation, drabness, and conformity on the other, the designer in the machine arts walks a narrow and uncomfortable path.

Architecture and civil engineering

If we find it awkward, because of certain limitations inherent in the nature of things, to approach machine design from an esthetic point of view, there is another field in which we need not feel so inhibited. This is the field of architecture and civil engineering. Here freedom and restraint go hand in hand, beauty and utility truly coalesce, and art and technics are wedded.

Although architecture and engineering are thought of today as two different professions, the distinction is of relatively recent origin. The Greek *architekton* (arch-technician) and the Roman *architectus* were designers and master builders in the widest sense, as was the medieval *ingeniator* (maker of ingenious devices, or engines of war). The artist-architect-engineer of the Renaissance was a man of unlimited interests and talents, best personified by the fabulous Leonardo da Vinci. But in the eighteenth century, as scientific theory came for the first time to be applied to practical problems of design, a breach appeared between the designer of buildings, who continued to rely on centuries-old techniques while seeking to achieve new artistic effects, and the designer of bridges, roads, and other public works, who used new engineering principles to achieve practical ends, often with little regard for esthetics. In England, around 1750, John Smeaton started referring to himself as a "civil engineer," and before long the distinction between architect and engineer was established throughout the Western world.

For the past two hundred years the relationship between these two professions, or two branches of the same profession, has been erratic and at times bizarre. Until well into the nineteenth century the architect went his own way designing buildings with classically pleasing proportions and applying to them a variety of Greek friezes, Roman pilasters, and Renaissance statuary. John Ruskin, a respected authority, preached the doctrine that a structure was "mere building" until graced by works of art. At the same time engineers were doggedly going about their own work, spotting the landscape with factories, mines, railways, and other assorted blemishes.

In the second half of the nineteenth century the development of structural steel and Portland cement suddenly opened up new vistas for the engineer, and in a burst of creative exuberance he designed and built some of the most marvelous bridges, towers, and buildings the world has ever seen. The architect looked on, first in amazement, then with increasing fascination. The Crystal Palace in 1851, the Brooklyn Bridge in 1883, the Paris Hall of Machines and Mr. Eiffel's tower in 1889, Louis Sullivan's Transportation Building at the Chicago World's Fair in 1893—each made an indelible impression on the architectural consciousness. Then, as the twentieth century began, what we now call modern architecture made its appearance. The engineer had done the groundwork, but the architect stole the show. Such cultural heroes as Frank Lloyd Wright and Le Corbusier were hailed as founders of the new art form. As for the engineer, he was quickly relegated to a subordinate role. And down to the present day this has been much the way it has been in the design of buildings: the architect rules, developing his overall concept and then hiring an engineer to provide for structural stability and mechanical services. On rare occasions the roles are reversed, as when the engineer hires an architect to dress up the exterior facade of a strictly engineering structure such as a pump house.

In recent years there have been signs that a renaissance of engineering design genius is taking place, inspired and made possible by new advances in metallurgy, structural concrete design, and mathematical analysis. The soaring stadiums of P. L. Nervi and the latticed domes of Buckminster Fuller serve notice that the engineer is not content to merely calculate while others create.

In the design of buildings, however, it appears likely that the architect will maintain his dominant position. His education is built around human needs and traditions—cultural and esthetic, as well as physical—which remain the central consideration, after all, in this field. Occasionally engineering inspiration may stand forth in bold relief—the skeleton may set the mood for the body, as it were—but in the long run it is architecture that will absorb engineering innovations, and not vice versa.

Still, there is an area in which the engineer is a match for the architect, and in many ways his master. When it is not buildings alone that are being planned, but entire communities, states, river basins, even continents, then the engineer bows to no one. This field of endeavor, which encompasses architecture, city planning, civil engineering, and much more is beginning to be known as *environmental engineering*. The engineer comes naturally by his interest in this field because of his training in highway and railway construction, mining, hydraulics and water supply, flood control, irrigation, sanitation, and a host of other specialties. The architect is vitally interested also, but rather "from the inside out," since he starts with his concern for single buildings and residential communities. But in its widest sense, environmental planning is beyond the technical capacities of the architect. The vital question then becomes, is it beyond the artistic capacities of the engineer?

For there is no mistaking the fact that the planning of environment is in great measure the planning of life, and such planning is an art far more than a science. Yet it is an art for which, in this complicated and overpopulated age, only the engineer has learned the essential techniques. It would be a cruel joke if, in learning the techniques, we have blunted our ability to apply them artistically. With no formulas to rely on, will we be able to strike a balance between utility and beauty, efficiency and fancy, grandeur and delicacy, modernity and tradition, speed and leisureliness? Will we be able to reconcile city with country, farm with suburb, factory with forest? Will we be able to design a new world with nothing to guide us but our own taste?

The taste of the engineer

There can be no doubt but that the world as it is developing will more and more reflect the taste of the engineer. In the tumultuous, largely unplanned growth of the past two hundred years, we have already made our mark on the landscape. In the years ahead, when an increased amount of technological planning appears to be the only alternative to chaos, our influence will be immeasurably increased.

Taste is said to be something that can't be argued about—*de gustibus non disputandum est*—and no doubt this is true in the case of elemental, physical preferences, such as for a favorite color. But when it comes to the cultivation of a taste for the beautiful and the meaningful and the valuable, then there is really nothing about which it is more worth arguing. John Dewey has put it this way:

> The formation of a cultivated and effectively operative good judgment or taste with respect to what is esthetically admirable, intellectually acceptable and morally approvable is the supreme task set to human beings by the incidents of experience.[5]

The *foundation* of good taste must be a familiarity with those masters whose insight, sensitivity, and talent—in short, whose genius—has enabled them to see penetratingly into nature and the human condition and to convey their special vision to their fellow men. The engineer who seeks enjoyment, understanding, and inspiration in the study of the fine arts cannot help but reflect his esthetic experiences in his work and in his life.

Recommended reading

Lewis Mumford, *Art and Technics* (Columbia University Press 9) is the outstanding work on this topic. A slim volume, based on lectures given by Mr. Mumford at Columbia

University in 1951, it is informed, humane, and absorbing. A bit pessimistic, perhaps, about the prospects for the human spirit in the modern age, Mr. Mumford is far from being a petulant critic of technology. His misgivings are based on sound knowledge and moving sensibility. This is one of the few works cited in this book which is required reading for the civilized engineer.

A fine book, amply illustrated, is Herbert Read, *Art and Industry* (Indiana University Press MB32). This book reviews the principles of industrial design both historically and theoretically, giving many interesting examples.

In Wylie Sypher (ed.), *Art History, An Anthology of Modern Criticism* (Vintage Books V243), there are two selections recommended in connection with this chapter: Rudolf Wittkower, "Architectural Principles in the Age of Humanism," and Francis D. Klingender, "Art and the Industrial Revolution."

On the planning of communities for human needs see Frank Lloyd Wright, *The Living City* (Mentor Books MT470) and Paul and Percival Goodman, *Communitas* (Vintage Books V174).

There is no shortage of excellent books about architecture. A few of them: Sigfried Giedion, *Space, Time, and Architecture* (Harvard University Press, 1962); John Gloag, *Guide to Western Architecture* (Macmillan, 1959); Talbot Faulkner Hamlin, *Architecture Through the Ages* (Putnam, 1953); Nikolaus Pevsner, *An Outline of European Architecture* (Penguin Books A109). Useful and attractive volumes dealing with outstanding individual modern architects can be found in series such as *Masters of World Architecture* and *Makers of Contemporary Architecture* (both published by George Braziller).

Henry Adams, *Mont-Saint-Michel and Chartres* (Anchor Books A166, and other editions) is a classic study of the medieval cathedrals and the religious and social forces which created them.

A leading engineer-builder of our age, Pier Luigi Nervi, expresses his philosophy in the handsomely illustrated *Aesthetics and Technology in Building* (Harvard University Press, 1965). *Twentieth Century Engineering*, published by The Museum of Modern Art in New York City, is a magnificent catalogue of the photographs that appeared in the museum's exhibition of the same title.

For intelligent discussion of beauty in the public domain, see Laurance B. Holland (ed.), *Who Designs America* (Anchor Books A523). This anthology, based on a conference on Design in America held at Princeton University, contains contributions by notables from the academic, artistic, and political communities.

The relationship between art and design is reviewed briefly in the pamphlet *Modern Art in Your Life* by Robert Goldwater and Rene d'Harnoncourt (The Museum of Modern Art, New York), and in depth in *Vision and Design* by Roger E. Fry (Meridian Books M33).

The six volumes of the *Vision + Value* series, edited by Gyorgy Kepes (George Braziller, Inc., 1966), contain essays by eighty-four distinguished natural and social scientists, architects, artists, and critics from a dozen countries. The interrelationship of art, science, and technology in the area of design and perception is treated exhaustively in this remarkable project.

CHAPTER NINE

The World
of the Fine Arts

We have spoken of the art that stems from craftsmanship, the desire to make objects of everyday use as pleasing to the eye as possible. This art has expressed itself since earliest times in pottery, weaving, and glassmaking, in the fabrication of tools and utensils, and in the construction of buildings. In every culture men have been moved to embellish, to shape, and to color—to add beauty to what has often been a drab and hostile environment. This is the sort of art that we engineers understand best. This is the tradition to which we contribute when we design with a deft hand and a sensitive eye.

The true artist and his mission

There is a different sort of art, however, created by men whose aims are deeper, purer, and more ambitious than those of the artisan. The true artist is not content with making the world more attractive. He seeks nothing less than to define the meaning of the universe, to understand the nature of things. His method is to explore the world as it manifests itself in visible forms. He searches for order, harmony, and meaning, and having found them, both in his environment and within his being, he attempts to share his vision with us. Michelangelo spoke of "liberating the figure from the marble that imprisons it." Just so does every artist intuitively perceive in the marble or on the canvas an image which he struggles to bring into being, his purpose being to have his audience share his insight. As he struggles, as he works with his chosen medium, his ideal conception is clarified and modified by the nature of his material and by the instinctive movements of his hand.

The insight, the private vision of each artist is unique. One may be concerned with the dignity of man, another with the beauty of nature, another with the glory of God, and another with the rhythm of a line. Essentially each artist seeks to create in us an emotional state, a mood, a sense of wonder or discovery or recognition.

The appreciation of art

Such emotional states cannot be expressed verbally. This is why so much nonsense is written and spoken about art. Since we are verbal creatures, we cannot resist trying to express in words the inexpressible. A harmless enough pastime, surely, unless we let the words form a screen between us and direct apprehension of the work of art. And who can deny that familiarity with the technical problems of art, as well as knowledge of the cultural background of the artist, contributes greatly to our ability to appreciate a work of art?

"Appreciation" is a tepid word, and "art appreciation" a phrase totally lacking in excitement. Yet excitement is what we should expect from art. Line, rhythm, mass, form, structure, proportion, perspective, space, tone, shading, color, light—these are what make up a work of art, and these are the concepts which we are asked to appreciate. But it is the artist's vision, his passion, if you will, that we must sense, or the viewing of art becomes trivial.

The arts of all civilizations are spread out before us in the museums and galleries of our nation. Although some are more pertinent than others, no doubt, there is enrichment to be found in all periods and in all cultures. As Herbert Read has said:

> The ultimate values of art transcend the individual and his time and circumstance . . . . In expressing his intuition the artist will use materials placed in his hands by the circumstances of his time: at one period he will scratch on the walls of his cave, at another he will build or decorate a temple or a cathedral, at another he will paint on canvas for a limited circle of connoisseurs. The true artist is indifferent to the materials and conditions imposed upon him. He accepts any conditions, so long as they can be used to express his will-to-form. Then in the wider mutations of history his efforts are magnified or diminished, taken up or dismissed, by forces which he cannot predict, and which have very little to do with the values of which he is the exponent. It is his faith that those values are nevertheless among the eternal attributes of humanity.[1]

Primitive art

Within the past few decades there has developed in our culture a sympathetic understanding of primitive art. Art that once was disparaged because it is not accurately representational is now recognized as being in no way inferior to the more polished art of advanced civilizations. In primitive societies the artist is moved to express his fear, his superstitious dread. He seeks magical control of his animal prey and his human enemies; he worships strength and fertility. These emotional states he portrays most effectively in the distorted masks, drawings, and carved figures with which we are familiar. His aim is not to copy or to idealize the world about him. His skill, his artistic genius, is directed toward other ends, and his achievements have been remarkable. There is a realistic impulse, true, the most extraordinary examples of which are to be found in stone-age cave paintings. But even where realism exists in primitive art, it is subject to an exaggeration that expresses the artist's emotional state and his magical intent.

Ancient Egypt

Most of the Egyptian art which has been preserved comes from tombs and temples. It strikes us as formal and stiff, particularly if we contrast it with primitive art. But this is appropriate enough, since in ancient Egypt men had escaped from the frenzied insecurity of a tribal hunting life into an ordered agricultural society, dominated by a hierarchic priesthood and a deified pharoah. We are repelled by the rigid, inhuman quality of Egyptian art, but impressed by its dignity. The pyramids set the tone, colossal and austere, which is carried out in the temples and the monumental statuary. In the wall paintings we get a flavor of everyday life, but here, too, all is controlled by formal artistic rules which hardly changed over the course of hundreds of years. The more important figures are drawn larger than the others; the heads, arms, and legs are shown from the side, and the bodies and the eyes are seen from the front. These strange representations do not indicate an ignorance of anatomy or a lack of skill, but rather express the completely stylized and static quality of that impressive but forbidding civilization.

Mesopotamian art resembles the Egyptian in many respects, but in that much more fluid and disordered part of the world the artists were free to give some emotional expression to their statues and reliefs. In Egyptian art we seek in vain for a departure from impassivity.

Greece and the concept of beauty

It is the Greeks who introduced the concept of beauty to the world. Of course earlier peoples were not blind to esthetic pleasures, but it is in Greece that we first find men freed both from superstition and political absolutism, men who gloried in their personal artistic impulses.

Philosophically, as we have seen, the Greeks were inclined to be idealists, and believed that there existed perfect forms and relationships. In their art, as in their philosophy, they sought to achieve insight into the nature of this perfection. Beauty, as they defined it, is the visible reflection of ultimate truth, the equivalent of moral goodness.

Their sculpture, architecture, pottery, and the little painting that has survived reflect a striking sense of proportion. Greek artists discovered the geometrical proportion known as the "golden section," which has been treated with veneration by artists and art critics of many times and places. (Cut a finite line so that the shorter part is to the longer part as the longer part is to the whole; roughly the proportion is 5 to 8.) They sought to create perfectly formed human beings in poses noble and serene. Thus they expressed both their admiration for man, that most sublime being, and their belief in the absolute, geometric nature of beauty.

With the Greeks the concepts of classical art were shaped, and they have remained a pervasive influence through all subsequent ages. The next time we look at a Greek statue and fall under the spell of its serenity and marvelous balance, we can remind ourselves that this is where the concept of beauty as we know it was born.

Yet is there not something aloof about such poise and such perfection? Where are the blemishes, the anguish, and the humor that makes us human? In their art as in their philosophy and literature we find that the Greeks admired only that which is graceful and elegant. They were aristocrats to the core.

The sacred art of Byzantium

The main current of Western art flowed from Greece to Rome, and, when Rome fell, to the eastern Roman empire, Byzantium. From its founding by Constantine in 330 until its fall to the Turks in 1453, Constantinople was the center of a mighty civilization, and from the seventh to the twelfth centuries, particularly, it was the center of a noble art. In museums, as we come from the halls of Greek and Roman statuary, moving toward the Renaissance art, we pass by paintings of saints and madonnas and angels, rigidly posed, their heads surrounded by circular halos of gold, their eyes staring blankly out of somber faces. This is Byzantine art, and our first impulse is to call it awkward and lifeless and to pass on quickly. But if we stop to view it on its own terms we may begin to feel differently. These artists were not interested in glorifying the human body. To them the ideals of classical art were pagan, the search for pure esthetic pleasures meaningless. Their attention was directed toward the divine rather than the human. Looked at as sacred art, the stiffness of the Byzantine style takes on a super-human quality, the halos and other symbols are bestowed with new significance. The very formality and abstractness of Byzantine art bespeaks its rejection of earthly ways and its devotion to the heavenly. This is true of its mosaics, sculpture, and architecture as well as of its paintings.

In discussing literature we spoke of our right to avoid the difficult and the dated because of the many demands on our time. In the fine arts we are under no such pressure—in minutes we can become acquainted with an artistic creation, while a comparable literary work might take hours or days. Happily, the ideals and faiths of bygone cultures are often more readily transmitted visually than in words. The art of the past, particularly such an alien art as the Byzantine, gives us a unique opportunity to stretch our sensibilities and to enrich our spirit. Even Oriental art, which we do not have space to deal with here, has much to say to us, whereas we usually find Oriental literature obscure and Oriental music cacophonous.

The Middle Ages: Romanesque and Gothic

In western Europe during the early Middle Ages, elements of classic art, Byzantine art, and native barbarian crafts combined to make the style we know as *Romanesque*. The art of this period is best known to us through exquisite illuminations of Bible manuscripts, and through church architecture, which featured the round arch, the semicircular barrel vault, and decorative sculpture.

Western art of the later Middle Ages, starting about 1150, is called *Gothic*. As the medieval towns grew in size and importance, a new and secular energy began to manifest itself. The manuscript illuminator moved out of the isolation of the monastery, and was likely to be working under the patronage of royalty or nobility. Private prayer books, psalters, and books of hours became popular, and in these the artist was freed from the restrictions of biblical subjects, and was able to illustrate the prayers with scenes drawn from contemporary life. Figures began to have a softer, more natural look, and shading was used to achieve a somewhat three-dimensional appearance. In sculpture, too, although religion was still the motivating force, we find a tinge of humanistic feeling.

The dominant art form of the Gothic period was architecture, and the cathedrals built during this time are among the most glorious achievements of mankind. The pointed arch, vaulting ribs, and buttresses—these were the technical developments which made the great structures possible. But the integration of interior and exterior, the fusion of beauty and function, create an emotional effect on the beholder far transcending admiration for technical genius. Magnificent stained-glass windows epitomize the radiant art of that age of faith.

Portents of a new age

The delicately framed Gothic cathedral was developed in northern France and spread throughout most of Europe. In Italy, however, churches kept their solid walls, and the painting of murals was developed to a high art. About 1300 an extraordinary Italian mural painter appeared who heralded the coming of a new artistic era. Giotto (1266?–1337) painted religious subjects, as had his predecessors, but his figures are different in a subtle but all-important way. By facial expressions, postures, and gestures they show that they are alive and in the grip of real emotions. For all that we have said about accepting sacred art on its own terms, it cannot be denied that the Byzantine and medieval artists ignored much of what we consider to be most precious in the world. It was inevitable that the artistic spirit should move away from religious stylization and austerity.

The next great stride was made in Flanders by the van Eyck brothers, Hubert (1365?–1426) and Jan (1385?–1441). They employed a then little-used medium, oil paint. Previously, painters had worked almost entirely in tempera (earth or mineral pigments moistened with water and then mixed with an albuminous substance such as egg white) or in fresco (applying colors to wet plaster). But more important than the new material was the van Eycks' discovery that our view of the world is affected by the way light is absorbed or reflected by different surfaces. Also as light passes through the air it is modified; distant objects appear hazier, paler, and bluer than close ones. Brightness and shadow, glow and mistiness—these are the characteristics of our natural world of light and air, the world that was now about to be explored in depth by the artist. With the van Eycks we also begin to find attention being paid to natural scenery and to interior furnishings. The painting of portraits, ignored by artists whose eyes were on the heavens, begins to come into its own.

The van Eycks, although they opened windows to the real world, are still classified as "Late Gothic" painters. Their figures have not yet achieved the flexibility, the strength, or the elasticity of facial expression which are the hallmarks of the Renaissance. Other North European masters of this time were Hans Memling (1430?–1494) and Hieronymus Bosch (1450?–1516), whose nightmarish fantasies remind us of some of the surrealistic painting of our own era.

The Italian Renaissance

The Renaissance, for reasons we discussed in Chapter 3, began in Italy. Artistically its center was in Florence, where the patronage of the Medici was an important stimulus. Rebellion against the medieval spirit came naturally to this society of prospering merchant princes, and the tradition of classical antiquity lay as close as the nearest ruin. It was the Italians who looked back to the glories of ancient Rome and scornfully labeled the years since its fall "Middle Ages." They, too, named the art of recent years "Gothic" after the barbarian plunderers of Rome.

The artists of the Italian Renaissance were not irreligious. On the contrary, most of them were devout. The church played an important part in their lives, not only as a cultural force, but also as a patron. Nevertheless they shared the prevailing mood of adventurousness, interest in the natural world, and confidence in human ingenuity. This prompted them to experiment, to expand their horizons, to study with new interest and affection the real word and, in particular, the body and the emotions of man. They slowly extended the scope of their subject matter beyond the traditional madonnas, crucifixions, and adorations, to include scenes of battles and ancient legends and portraits of their contemporaries. Landscapes and still lifes were not known, but more and more the scenic background shows respectful study of nature. Undoubtedly the Renaissance artists felt that the loving exploration of God's world was an undertaking more sacred than profane.

During the fifteenth century Italian artists made great strides in understanding the workings of the human body. Faces began to reflect personality and character. The rules of scientific perspective were discovered. Perceptiveness and technique were developed to new heights. Outstanding artists of the 1400s, the *Quattrocento,* were Fra Angelico (1387–1455), Masaccio (1401–1428?), Paolo Uccello (1396?–1475), Fra Filippo Lippi (1406–1469), and Sandro Botticelli (1444?–1510), whose shimmering *The Birth of Venus* is one of the most famous of paintings.

Leonardo, Michelangelo, and Raphael

In the following century, the *Cinquecento,* we come to the "High Renaissance" and those three towering geniuses Leonardo da Vinci (1452–1519), Michelangelo Buonarroti (1475–1564), and Raphael (1483–1520). Leonardo, as we know, was as great an engineer, inventor, and scientist as he was an artist. This many-faceted master is unique in the history of civilization. As an artist he is best known for *Mona Lisa,* the haunting and evocative painting that has captured the world's imagination. But he is seen to best advantage in the sketches in his *Notebooks,* where we find him exploring the inner nature of thousands of phenomena, living and mechanical.

To Michelangelo the world was not an organism to be investigated. This tempestuous artist saw the universe as the creation of almighty God, and man as the inheritor of the spark of divine life. He painted and carved superhuman creatures, mightier and more perfect than any living person. His statues of Moses and David are world famous, and his painting of *The Creation of Adam* on the Sistine Chapel ceiling is the definitive artistic statement of this theme. Leonardo was the more versatile genius, but Michelangelo undeniably the more inspired artist.

Compared with these two titans, Raphael, for all his admitted genius, seems mild indeed. His many paintings of Madonna and Child are harmonious and tranquil, rich in color and softly modeled, but almost too sweet for our contemporary taste.

The Venetian School

The wealthy city-state of Venice faced toward the Orient, and in the Venetian painters we find a deepened sensuousness and richness of color which differentiates them from the masters of Rome and Florence. In Giorgione (1478?–1511) we find these qualities combined with a sense of melancholy reverie. This style influenced the work of the great Titian (1477–1576), master of the portrait.

Eventually Venetian painting came under the influence of what is called "Mannerism," a style that differed greatly from the art of the High Renaissance. Motivated to a great extent by the Counter-Reformation's interest in ridding Italy of humanist influence, the Mannerists abandoned classical ideals of perfection, and were given to dramatic composition, distortion of shape, and a spectacular and emotional use of color and light.

Their subject matter was less secular, more dramatically theological or supernatural. This style is seen in the works of Correggio (1494–1534) of Parma, and was developed by the Venetian Tintoretto (1518–1594). Another Venetian, Paolo Veronese (1528–1588), whose works exemplify Mannerist use of color, nevertheless worked very much under the influence of principles of the High Renaissance. The mammoth canvasses of Tintoretto and Veronese are judged to represent a decline from the heights of the Renaissance. Be this as it may, for all their opulence—or maybe because of it—they are undeniably impressive.

El Greco and the art of Spain

Trained in the Venetian tradition, perhaps by Titian himself, was the genius from Crete known as El Greco (1541–1614). This unique artist spent most of his mature years in Spain, which was at that time becoming the mightiest power in Europe. El Greco's paintings are noted for their passionate, spiritual quality. His luminous, elongated figures, draped in rich blue and purple robes are distinctive and readily identifiable.

Other Spanish painters of this period fell prey to the emotional excesses of the Counter-Reformation. The Church had hitherto been a source of inspiration and a dependable patron. But in sixteenth- and seventeenth-century Spain gloomy mysticism and a macabre obsession with martyrdom had an adverse effect on artistic development. Only the great Diego Velasquez (1599–1660), painter to the court of Philip IV, maintained the delicate balance between passion and intellect. But chronologically this takes us ahead of our story.

The Northern Renaissance

The influence of Italian Renaissance art soon spread to the north. Albrecht Dürer (1471–1528) showed the way, combining the monumental quality of Italian painting with an attention to detail that was in the Flemish tradition. He was a master of the engraving and the woodcut, and because of the many copies that could be made of these works, his influence was widespread. Hans Holbein the Younger (1497–1543) traveled from his native Germany to England, where he became court painter to Henry VIII. His portraits are unmistakably northern in feeling; but when they are compared with the portraits of earlier artists such as the van Eycks, the majestic influence of the Italian Renaissance can be discerned.

In Flanders, Pieter Breughel the Elder (1525–1569) made landscape the most important feature of many of his paintings. He peopled his scenes with peasants at work and at play. His implied comments about humanity are cynical and amusing, but strangely disturbing. His provocative social and psychological satire have earned him considerable popularity in the twentieth century.

Baroque art

Renaissance art is marked both by an exuberance and by a restraint born of respect for classical art and strict adherence to contemporary views of color and perspective. As the sixteenth century drew to a close the exuberance was undiminished, the restraint all but forgotten. The art of the seventeenth and early eighteenth century is known as "Baroque," after the Portugese word for a lustrous but imperfect pearl. Baroque architecture and furniture are heavy, exaggerated, and richly ornamented. Sculpture of this period, also, is swollen and flamboyant. Baroque painting is more varied and difficult to define, but in general it, too, tends toward restlessness and overstatement.

In Rome about 1600 Caravaggio (1565?–1609) created a stir with his "naturalistic" style. In his paintings lifelike figures, brilliantly illuminated as if with spotlights, seem to be caught in the midst of movement. The artistic term for strong contrast between light and shade is *chiaroscuro*. Extravagant use of *chiaroscuro* for dramatic effect is called *tenebroso,* and this is the technique that Caravaggio introduced to painting at the start of the Baroque period.

Peter Paul Rubens (1577–1640) studied for eight years in Italy, where he was much impressed with Caravaggio's work. Upon returning to his native Flanders, he quickly became the most popular painter in Europe. Among the most prolific artists who ever lived, he set up a huge studio where apprentices did much of the work on canvases that he designed, supervised, finished, and signed. His profusion of portraits and mythical, religious, and historical scenes are almost too sumptuous for our taste. Rubens and his disciple, Anthony Van Dyck (1599–1641), represent Baroque art in all its richness, color, and movement.

The Dutch masters

Whereas Flemish art developed in a Catholic society under ecclesiastical and noble patrons, in neighboring Holland the first great painters of the Protestant world were appearing. The prosperous burghers enjoyed portraits, landscapes, still lifes, and "genre" scenes of ordinary middle-class family life. They relished the world about them in its actuality—unadorned, unidealized.

We have had occasion to discuss the natural antipathy that exists between the creative writer and bourgeois society. This mutual hostility exists in the fine arts no less than in literature. Surely primitive art, classical art, religious art, and much of modern art are by implication critical of middle-class values. And the middle class traditionally has been suspicious of the artist and slow to understand him.

But Dutch painting of the seventeenth century is proof that, under certain conditions, the solid, pedestrian, bourgeois world can give birth to, love, and nourish great art.

Among the Dutch portraitists Frans Hals (1580?–1666) was a favorite, and remains one still. His cavaliers and buxom lasses are irresistably vigorous and jolly, brought to life by a dashing, "unfinished" brush stroke. Among the great Dutch landscape artists are Jacob van Ruisdael (1628?–1682) and Meyndaert Hobbema (1638–1709). Famous for gay "genre" scenes of peasant life is Jan Steen (1626–1679); famous for tranquil, beautifully illuminated interior scenes of home life are Jan Vermeer (1632–1675) and Pieter de Hooch (1629–1677?).

The greatest artist in the Dutch school, and one of the greatest artists of all time, was Rembrandt van Rijn (1606–1669). He absorbed all that Caravaggio had taught about the dramatic use of light, and then added his touch of genius, illuminating his figures spiritually from within. From the lovely, straightforward portraits of his early years to the poignant and powerful works of his old age, this magnificent artist is consistently able to please and to move us.

France and Rococo art

In the eighteenth century, with the glitter of Versailles at its brightest, we find the emergence of a new style, called "Rococo." Amusing, gay, restless, and decorative to excess, the new style was both an expression of the frivolity of the French aristocracy and the development to extremes of the Baroque tradition. In architecture and in interior decoration Rococo is known to us as *Louis Quinze* and *Louis Seize*.

The prominent painters of the period were Antoine Watteau (1684–1721), Francois Boucher (1703–1770), and Jean-Honoré Fragonard (1732–1806). Their boudoir scenes and sentimental, bucolic idylls, featuring courtiers as make-believe shepherds and shepherdesses, are either ludicrous or enchanting, depending upon one's mood. A more sober tradition was kept alive in the still lifes and genre scenes of Jean-Baptiste Siméon Chardin (1699–1779).

Neoclassicism

As the aristocracy of France moved toward its inevitable doom, there developed a new style that was "anti-Rococo" in feeling. Austere and disciplined, featuring meticulous surfaces and formal compositions, harking back to antiquity for political and social, as well as esthetic, inspiration, this style is known as "Neoclassicism." Its most famous proponent was Jacques Louis David (1748–1825), who became the "official" painter of the French Revolution. His *Death of Marat,* showing the murdered revolutionary leader dead in his bathtub, is a landmark in the history of art—and in the history of civilization.

David's outstanding disciple, Jean Auguste Dominique Ingres (1780–1867), carried the Neoclassic style to its fullest realization. Discarding the florid brushwork of the Baroque masters, he stressed line, balance, and restraint.

The almost photographic quality of the work of David and Ingres enhances its beauty and at the same time diminishes its creative impact. With the invention of photography in the early 1800s the impulse toward such exactness was destined to diminish. Even without the competition of photography it was clear that the cold precision of Neoclassicism was a dead end. At the beginning of the nineteenth century the fever of Romanticism was sweeping Europe. The fine arts were soon to feel the effect.

English art and Romanticism

Romanticism, it will be remembered, flourished early in English poetry. This is also true of English painting. Note that we have not yet mentioned a single English artist. For all their literary brilliance the English had never developed great creative talent in the fine arts. Outstanding painters at the English court, such as Holbein and Van Dyck, had come from the continent.

In the eighteenth century English art finally came into its own with the elegant portraits of Joshua Reynolds (1723–1792) and Thomas Gainsborough (1727–1788). William Hogarth (1697–1764) also achieved fame for his portraits, but even more for his satirical "stories," the best known of which is the series of scenes called *The Rake's Progress*.

As the nineteenth century dawned, Romantic art emerged in the development of English landscape painting. Gainsborough had shown the way with the beautiful settings in which he had placed the subjects of his portraits. John Constable (1776–1837) brought into play the full force of Romantic sensibility and lavished it on the wondrous English landscape. His views of Salisbury Cathedral, along with many other glowing scenes, have become a haven, a precious part of the dream world of all English-speaking people.

Joseph M. W. Turner (1775–1851) in his colossal landscapes and seascapes went even farther in the romantic glorification of nature. His canvases, ablaze with a supernatural light, are truly awe-inspiring. According to one critic, his work is "perhaps the greatest revelation ever made of the power and majesty of nature."[2] According to another: "Like an overzealous organist, Turner has pulled a few stops too many, so that the music becomes deafening."[3]

Spain and France in the Romantic age

In Spain, Francisco Goya (1746–1828) resisted the Neoclassic trend, and developed a unique style consisting of Baroque technique and Romantic sensibility. His love of liberty and abhorrence of war give his works a lasting popularity.

The Romantic movement in painting is most eloquently summed up in the works of Theodore Géricault (1791–1824) and Eugene Delacroix (1799–1863). Rearing horses, raging seas, flowing, exotic costumes—this is the stuff of which these two French artists compounded their emotion-charged canvases. The Neoclassicist Ingres was hard put to maintain his preeminence in the face of such competition, and eventually Delacroix surpassed him in popularity.

Two other French artists of this period deserve mention: Honoré Daumier (1808–1879) and Gustave Courbet (1819–1877). Daumier is known best for his lithograph caricatures, but he was also a skilled painter in whose work savage wit is combined with great compassion for the underprivileged. Courbet was prominent in the school that is known as "Realism." Photographic in detail, his paintings show peasants and workers at their everyday tasks. This sober and unsophisticated approach to art has had its adherents in each subsequent generation. As in literature, its moral intent is worthy enough; but too often it results in works more pedestrian than inspired.

Impressionism

Since the Renaissance there has been a steady trend in art away from the monumental toward the personal. From Egyptian times through the Middle Ages most art was created on a large scale for display in public places. Although this tradition has never disappeared, we find art becoming increasingly intimate, the personality of the artist increasingly important. Culturally this reflects the growth of democracy and emphasis on the significance of the individual. Practically it explains why painting, the most intimate of the arts, has flourished, and why the small canvas, suitable for hanging in the home, has become so popular.

This trend toward the personal is evident in the next impor-

tant stage in the history of art, "Impressionism." The painters
of this school sought to capture fleeting atmospheric effects,
transitory visual impressions, and an evanescent "reality" born
of individual perception.

The Impressionists left the even lighting of the studio and
went out into the blazing sun. Today we are so used to the
thought of painting outdoors that we are surprised to learn that,
except for Constable, practically all earlier painters of importance had worked exclusively in the studio. Painting directly
from nature, the Impressionists paid little heed to contour and
line. With undisguised brush strokes, in brilliant colors, they
recreated a world of blur and glitter, well known to the perceptive eye, but never before seen on canvas.

Édouard Manet (1832–1883) is known as a precursor of
Impressionism. Where previous painters had used light and
shade to model their figures, Manet threw a brilliant light on
his subjects from the front, eliminating shadows. He obtained
form by using different patches of color.

Claude Monet (1840–1926), developed the technique of
"broken color." Instead of mixing colors on the palette, he placed
raw colors in dabs next to each other, letting the colors be
mixed in the air or in the eye of the beholder. This technique
was later carried to extremes in the *pointillism* of Georges Seurat
(1859–1891).

The most famous of the Impressionists was Auguste Renoir
(1841–1919), whose luscious, plump women and rosy-cheeked
children are familiar to even the most casual observer of art.
Other noted members of this school are Camille Pissarro (1830–
1903) and Alfred Sisley (1839–1899). Edgar Degas (1834–
1917) participated in the first Impressionist exhibition, held in
1874, but his devotion to drawing and to form, as evidenced in
his familiar paintings of ballet dancers, isolates him from other
members of this school. Henri de Toulouse-Lautrec (1864–
1901), like Degas, ignored the amorphous aspects of Impression-

ism, and did his arresting sketches of Parisian night life in sharp
black lines and flat color patterns.

Postimpressionism

The three outstanding painters known as "Postimpressionists"
are Paul Cézanne (1839–1906), Paul Gauguin (1848–1903),
and Vincent van Gogh (1853–1890). Although happy to adopt
many of the new techniques, none of these artists was satisfied
with the ephemeral "optical realism" of Impressionism. Cézanne
sought to define the strong, basic shapes which underlie surface
appearances. "You must see in nature," he said, "the cylinder,
the sphere, the cone." In his landscapes we begin to see the
emergence of abstract geometric figures. In his faces, in his in-
teriors, we begin to find distortion and faulty perspective. He is
groping toward an understanding of the essence of form.
Cézanne's dispassionate, intellectual approach reminds us of
classical art, although his vision is distinctly modern.

With Gauguin and van Gogh we find art moving in a very
different direction. These two emotional, individualistic artists
are known as precursors of "Expressionism." Their personal feelings are "expressed," are indeed the heart of their paintings.
Gauguin we know best for his Tahitian scenes. Simple and flat,
but undeniably powerful, they express both the enchantment
and the melancholy felt by the sophisticated artist in a primitive
setting. With van Gogh all is energy and movement. Frenzied
brush strokes and vibrant colors express his highly charged,
apocalyptic visions.

The approach to modern art

With the Postimpressionists, we enter upon two separate roads
that lead us into the world of modern art. One is objective, intellectual, abstract—the way of Cézanne; the other is subjective

and intensely emotional—the way of Gauguin and van Gogh. These are roads, as we have seen, that have their beginnings far back in the history of art.

One other road must be considered as we approach modern art—the way of fantasy. Henri Rousseau (1844–1910), a retired customs official who received no formal art training, created a series of canvases which first came to public attention in the late 1880s. Nothing quite like them had ever been seen before. *The Sleeping Gypsy,* with its silent desert and pale moon, its sleeping figure, lute, and phantom lion, is just such stuff as dreams are made of. The artist's fantasy has been expressed on canvas. For taking this step, it has been said that "Rousseau, more than anyone else, may be called the godfather of twentieth-century painting."[4]

Twentieth-century art, then, consists of three main schools: Abstraction, Expressionism, and Fantasy.

Expressionism

Expressionism developed first, appearing in Paris, where it was known as "Fauvism." At a 1904 showing of works by Henri Matisse (1869–1954) and other young unknowns, a critic coined the phrase, *les fauves,* "the wild beasts," which the artists happily adopted. The paintings of Matisse show us a world filtered through an artist's sensibility—simplified, distorted, worked into patterns, and fancifully colored. Individual objects are recognizable, but imaginatively transformed. They are not realistic, but neither are they abstract.

The Fauvists quickly became famous. Amedeo Modigliani (1884–1920) of Italy was one of many artists with similar goals attracted to Paris at this time. Georges Rouault (1871–1958) became a member of the group. From Fauvism Rouault was to go on to express deep religious feeling in a unique style featuring dark outlines and colors reminiscent of stained-glass windows.

Another Fauvist was Georges Braque (1882–1963), but he and his friend Pablo Picasso (1881–   ) were destined to branch off soon in a very different direction. Picasso, although not a Fauvist, was in Paris in 1904, poor and lonely, painting the wistful, expressionistic works of his "blue period."

By 1910 Expressionism had been adopted in Germany where the Russian-born Vasily Kandinsky (1866–1944) became its prime exponent. Between 1910 and 1913 Kandinsky developed the concept of "nonobjective" painting, in which color and line, without being representative of any actual object, were used as a means of representing "spiritual" states of mind. But most painters were not yet ready to turn their backs completely on representational art. After World War I the German Expressionists, most notably Max Beckmann (1884–1950), depicted their mood of despair in works of shocking bitterness.

Abstraction

Abstraction appeared in Paris about 1907 under the name of "Cubism." Picasso and Braque abandoned their expressionistic work to develop this new style. They carried Cézanne's search for form to its logical conclusion, twisting objects and turning them, seeing them simultaneously from several views, making them transparent, breaking, cutting, flattening and reconstructing them in new relationships, all as dictated by a disciplined artistic sensibility.

Along with Picasso and Braque, noted Cubists were Juan Gris (1887–1927), Fernand Leger (1881–1955), and Piet Mondrian (1872–1944). Mondrian moved deeper and deeper into the world of geometry until he left behind all connection with real objects. His clean white canvases marked out in rectangular patterns confronted the world with a radically new artistic concept. Through progressive stages of abstraction he had arrived at a nonobjective concern with pure proportion and balance.

Kandinsky, as we have noted, through progressive stages of Expressionism had arrived at a nonobjective concern with pure feeling.

The time was not distant when Abstraction and Expressionism would meet.

Fantasy

Out of dreams and out of the subconscious came the compelling works that have been grouped together under the term "Fantasy." Sometimes they were nightmare scenes that fill us with anxiety, such as the empty railroad station of *The Anxious Journey* by Giorgio de Chirico (1888–   ). Sometimes they were whimsical and capricious, such as the mechanical chirpers in the *Twittering Machine* of Paul Klee (1879–1940), or the wiggling and floating creatures in the *Carnival of Harlequin* of Joan Miró (1893–   ). Sometimes they were wistfully evocative of a vanished past as in *I and the Village* by Marc Chagall (1887–   ).

Out of this tradition came Surrealism, in which a very literal and realistic style is used to depict the wildest fantasies, the most sinister apprehensions. Important names in this style are Max Ernst (1891–   ), Yves Tanguy (1900–1955), and Salvador Dali (1904–   ), whose dripping watches have become a symbol of our age of anxiety.

Art among the "isms"

Very quickly the doctrines of Expressionism, Abstraction, and Fantasy intermingled. Indeed they were never really isolated from each other, any more than emotion, intellect, and imagination are isolated within a human being. The various styles borrowed from each other. Individual artists, most notably the great Picasso, experimented, changed, and showed the effects of many influences.

But for every movement toward unification among the styles, there was a countermovement toward fragmentation. New "isms" were very much in vogue. *Futurism* found its inspiration in the animation of life in a technological world. "The roaring automobile," proclaimed its founders, "is more beautiful than the *Winged Victory*."[5] The Futurists attempted to capture movement on canvas, giving us paintings that remind us of stroboscopic photos. *Dadaism* was founded to declare certain artists' disgust with the world and their intent to shock and outrage the public with works dictated by chance and impulse.

The art of America

So far we have not mentioned a single American artist, and with good reason, since until recently the outstanding artists of the Western world have all been Europeans. American painting of the colonial period has a certain charm, and in the last half of the nineteenth century some fine work was done by Winslow Homer (1836–1910), Thomas Eakins (1844–1916), and Albert Pinkham Ryder (1847–1917). Mary Cassatt (1845–1926) and James A. McNeill Whistler (1834–1903) were noted Americans, but they lived in Europe and painted as Europeans.

Skillful portrayers of city life in styles borrowing much from Impressionism were John Sloan (1871–1951) and Edward Hopper (1882–1967). In the 1930s there was a brief flurry of interest in the works of such "regionalists" as Grant Wood (1892–1942) of Iowa, John Steuart Curry (1897–1946) of Kansas, and Thomas Hart Benton (1889–   ) of Missouri. At the same time the world was impressed by the strong, revolutionary murals of the Mexicans Diego Rivera (1886–1957) and José Clemente Orozco (1883–1949).

However, it was not until after World War II that the art capital of the world shifted from Europe to the Western hemisphere, and in particular from Paris to New York. The shift occurred as a result of the rise of a new school, *Abstract Expressionism.*

The revival of sculpture

Before we go on to consider the latest trends in painting, let us take a quick look at the revival of sculpture in our time. Since the days of Michelangelo sculpture had steadily declined in importance, overshadowed by its sister art, painting.

The beginnings of its renaissance can be traced to Auguste Rodin (1840–1917). This great artist, under the influence of Romanticism and Impressionism, developed an immensely popular style. He abandoned the cold, impersonal smoothness of classical sculpture in favor of irregular surfaces which, under the play of light, reflected a sense of life and movement.

In the twentieth century, sculpture has evolved in tempo with all of the new cultural and artistic developments. Constantin Brancusi (1876–1957) adopted in his "Primevalism" the formal simplicity of primitive carvings. About 1910 he embarked on a new course of nonrepresentational work in marble and metal. He explored the self-contained perfection of the egg, and soaring vertical flight motifs in such propellerlike creations as *Bird in Space.* Jacques Lipchitz (1891–   ) dissected and reconstructed in the Cubist tradition. The bulbous abstractions of the human form by Henry Moore (1898–   ) show a concern for the organic as opposed to the geometric. Moore also introduced a new respect for his materials, "translating" from flesh and blood into stone rather than "reduplicating."

Alberto Giacometti (1901–1966) conveys a surrealistic effect in his tall, spindly figures and in his airy constructions of wood, glass, wire, and string. The rugged busts of Jacob Epstein (1880–1959) have done much to change our concept of what constitutes a good "likeness." Umberto Boccioni (1882–1916) created implied motion in sculpture by surrounding figures in mantels of aerial turbulence. Actual motion was introduced in the delicately balanced mobiles of Alexander Calder (1898–).

Abstract Expressionism

We have noted how nonobjective painting developed out of both Abstraction and Expressionism. Abstract Expressionism, as its name implies, was a joining of these two forces, and produced the nonobjective painting that the average layman has puzzled over and come to know as "modern art." Jackson Pollock (1912–1956) achieved a direct visual recording of movement by dripping paint in surging patterns on huge canvases. Franz Kline (1910–1962), using a house painter's brush, attacked the canvas with broad, slashing strokes. Mark Rothko (1903–) confronts us with serene compositions, consisting of large, balanced areas of color. A few members of this school, notably Adolph Gottlieb (1903–) and Willem de Kooning (1904–), show us an occasional form that is recognizable. But in general this art consists of colors, shapes, and patterns, and nothing more. It is as "pure" as music, and seeks to evoke in us an emotional response without reference to any particular recognizable objects.

Pop art

Just as the public was beginning to get used to this new art —although not necessarily beginning to understand it—Pop art burst upon the scene. In the late 1950s and early 1960s the art world was confronted with the numbers, targets, and flags of Jasper Johns, the blown-up comic strips of Roy Lichtenstein, the soup cans of Andy Warhol, the plaster characters of George Segal, the giant hamburgers of Claes Oldenburg. Equally unusual works were presented by Robert Rauschenberg, Larry Rivers, Jim Dine, and Tom Wesselman.

Is this the new art of our time? Are these artists "bold creators" showing us, "as if for the first time, the world we have always had about us but ignored . . . ."?[6] Do they "share . . . an intense passion for direct experience, for unqualified participation in the richness of our immediate world, whatever it may have become, for better or worse . . . ."?[7] Are they conducting "research . . . into ways of seeing more rigorously and precisely . . . ."?[8]

Are the Pop artists yea-sayers to democracy and the modern age, or are they alienated, deadpan, "cool," and ironic? Do their works contentedly "represent the epitome of the middle-class American ethic,"[9] or are they haunted by "an implication of absence . . . of human absence from a man-made environment . . . ."?[10]

And Op

Scarcely had the public begun to consider the implications of Pop art when suddenly, in 1965, everyone was taking about Op. This new art abandons the "things" that enchant the Pop artist and confronts us with geometric patterns that dazzle, with color combinations that make our eyes bulge. To what purpose? To make us "aware of the experience of perception and its corollary, that stimuli are shifting and ambiguous."[11] Certainly, but there is more to it than just a game of optical illusions and after-images. The search for new sensations, new revelations, and new truths in art has led the artist into the realm of science and technology. A critic has stated that "instead of the former comparison of abstract art with music there is an evocation of information theory." One op artist "is conscious of a likeness between his ranks of regular forms and the binary code of digital computers . . . . Reference, in a lyrical or offhand way, is to the point, the dot, as in punched cards and tapes."[12] The implications of such an art for engineers is most intriguing.

We engineers, by and large, are laymen in the world of the fine arts. We share with the general public a bewilderment, and occasional hostility, when confronted with the works of contemporary artists.

Yet in the development of Abstract Expressionism, Pop art, and particularly Op art, there is, side by side with an implied protest against technology, a strong "pro-technology attitude"[13] that should appeal to us. The study of physical objects, of substances and textures, of pure line and form and color, uncluttered with overt philosophical or emotional statements—is this not the sort of art that should be most fascinating to men of our profession? The new sculptures, welded and bolted, the gadgets that move mechanically, light up electrically, whistle electronically—are they not as much products of engineering as of art?

All this is true enough. There is an interest and amusement in contemporary art particularly compelling to the engineer. Yet this does not satisfy us. We are made uneasy by the absence of the recognizably *human* element. We are technologists, to be sure, but we are humanists as well. Our interest is not in technology for its own sake but rather as a means to the end of human fulfillment. This dichotomy has come up before in our discussion of the relationship of engineering to the philosophy of science. Without a sense of the value of human life, our professional work becomes mere tinkering.

The contemporary artist will reply, no doubt, that all artistic creation, no matter how empty of manifest signs of humanity, is a celebration of the human spirit. He also demands the right "to create a new world of form and space, existing apart from all previous experience of the tangible external world, and creating its own special logic as well as its own unique excitement."[14]

Of course the tradition of humanistic realism is not dead. The popular Andrew Wyeth is only one of many artists still exploring the visible and recognizable world. No doubt as the future unfolds there will be new styles and new approaches to old styles, evoking, and responding to, changes in our culture.

In the meanwhile, let us keep our eyes open and our imaginations spry. There is no need to be overly serious or literal, no need to be angered at even the most outlandish artistic creation. "Art is a lie," as Picasso has said, "a lie that makes us realize the truth."

Recommended reading

Two excellent series of introductory works are: *Time-Life Library of Art* (Time-Life Books) and *Seminars in Art* (Metropolitan Museum of Art, New York).

Two good one-volume works are: H. W. Janson, *History of Art* (Harry N. Abrams, 1962), and Francis Henry Taylor, *Fifty Centuries of Art* (Harper & Row, 1960).

There is an abundance of wonderful books of art reproductions. Among the best series: *Encyclopedia of World Art* (McGraw-Hill); *Library of Great Painters* (Harry N. Abrams); *Pelican History of Art* (Penguin Books); *The Phaidon Press Books* (Doubleday); and *The Skira Art Books* (Skira).

A valuable introduction to modern art is a booklet published by The Museum of Modern Art, New York: Alfred H. Barr, Jr., *What Is Modern Painting?* An excellent collection of essays about contemporary art is in Gregory Battcock (ed.), *The New Art* (Dutton D178).

Recommended viewing

No amount of reading, or even looking at reproductions, however excellent, can take the place of viewing real art works.

There are many fine museums throughout the nation. But for a gourmet feast of the best in the world's art, nothing can compare with a tour through the museums and galleries of New York City.

The Metropolitan Museum of Art has one of the great collections of the world. The Cloisters, in a beautiful setting high above the Hudson River, houses a superb collection of medieval art. The Frick Collection, displayed in a handsome mansion, is a veritable jewel containing some of the very best paintings of the fourteenth to the nineteenth centuries. The Museum of Modern Art and the Solomon R. Guggenheim Museum display the works of the greatest twentieth-century masters. At the Whitney Museum fine American art is to be seen. Among the many others where the special shows are usually outstanding: Asia House, the Brooklyn Museum, China House, the Gallery of Modern Art, the Jewish Museum, the Morgan Library, the Museum of American Folk Art, the Museum of Primitive Art, The New York Public Library, the Riverside Museum. Add to these the dozens of galleries showing the most prominent contemporary artists, and we can see that the artistic riches of the city are practically inexhaustible.

An added dividend is to be found in the architectural interest of the museum buildings themselves. Three of the most recent: Frank Lloyd Wright's Guggenheim, Edward Durrell Stone's Gallery of Modern Art, and, most handsome, Marcel Breuer's Whitney.

CHAPTER TEN

The Bridge
to Music:
Sound as Environment

Of all the arts, the one with which the average engineer is likeliest to be acquainted is music. This may seem odd until one considers that it probably holds true for people in all walks of life. For music is aggressive; it actively seeks out the ear and makes its presence felt. Books must be read, paintings must be viewed, plays must be attended; but music leaps out at us from radios and TV sets, and from loudspeakers in restaurants, airplanes, and building lobbies. It follows us into circuses and churches, banquets and ball games. It appears at almost every occasion of ceremony, whether religious or secular.

Yet the engineer's acquaintance with music goes far deeper than these casual encounters which we share with all men. For one thing, engineers are engaged in the design and manufacture of musical instruments. Composing may be the purest of the arts, but the actual performance of music consists of blowing, rasping, and striking on mechanisms which require exceptional technological skills to design and produce. "We have yet sufficiently to realize," says Lewis Mumford, "that the symphony orchestra is a triumph of engineering."[1]

Engineers also come to music by way of the science of acoustics. No longer are concert halls and auditoriums designed haphazardly so that the music performed in them is subjected to disconcerting echoes, distortions, and dead spots. The acoustical qualities of a hall are now carefully controlled by analysis of size and shape, and by the study and development of materials with special characteristics of sound absorption and reflection. Acoustical engineering is still in its infancy, and it has suffered some embarrassing failures. But, having learned from their mistakes, acoustical engineers are making noteworthy advances.

Still other engineers have approached music by way of electronics, a field which has advanced breathtakingly in recent years. Music is amplified, recorded, and broadcast electronically. On tape it is speeded up, slowed down, edited and spliced—even created. The ardent and delicate pursuit of "high fidelity" has all but obliterated, in some areas, the distinction between art and engineering.

Analysis and rapture

Perhaps most engineers, like most scientists, approach music through the doorway of mathematics, being attracted to balance and order wherever they find it. Mathematics and human emotions seem to have common origins in the elemental laws of nature. The rhythms of our lives, the very stuff of music and of all art—our breathing, our heartbeat, the cycles of hunger and satiety, vitality and fatigue, tension and release—are rooted in the same relationships of number and wavelength and energy which are at the core of mathematical science. The intellectual appreciation of music is a *conscious* awareness of the same tempos and proportions that stir our emotions subconsciously. Analysis and rapture are twin sisters, bound by ties we have not even begun to explore. Indeed the ancients regarded music as a science of measurement, to be classified with geometry, astronomy, and arithmetic. Musical order was considered to be a reflection of the harmony of the heavens and a bridge to the harmony of the soul.

Today, in keeping with the increasing isolation of art from life, music is widely thought of as nothing more than an agreeable pastime; and even where it is taken most seriously, a gulf has appeared between its artistic and scientific aspects and between its emotional and intellectual halves. This trend need not be considered irreversible. "It may well be," comments composer Paul Hindemith, "that the last word concerning the interdependence of music and the exact sciences has not been spoken."[2]

Sound as environment

In all of these areas—design of musical instruments, acoustics, electronics, and mathematics—music and engineering touch. But they are even more closely bound to each other by the common interest that they have in *sound as environment*. This interest is not limited to formal music, but embraces sound as men encounter it every moment of the day and night, sound as it is experienced continuously in the ocean of air in which we live. The composer is acutely conscious of the sounds about him—

the sounds of nature, the sounds of men, and the sounds of machines. All are raw material for his art.

The engineer has reason to be equally sensitive. For sound is every bit as important a part of human environment as are temperature, humidity, pollen count, and all the rest of the environmental phenomena which the engineer so carefully records and so earnestly attempts to control. Perhaps decibels are not as dangerous as smoke particles, but they are capable of doing real damage to health and character, damage which is all the more insidious for being difficult to evaluate. With the growth of industrial society the engineer has increasingly turned his attention to the problem of air pollution. It is now recognized that air can be polluted just as offensively by harsh, nerve-racking sound waves as it can by smoke.

The control of noise

Probably the biggest offenders against the peace and quiet of our communities are the vehicles of transportation. Jet planes make the areas around our airports practically uninhabitable. Trains and trucks rumble through the night, disturbing sleep wherever they go. Buses, fire engines, and other wheeled vehicles contribute to the havoc which characterizes our cities. Other sources of noise include factories, quarries, and power plants, although in these cases the disturbance is usually confined to those who actually work with the noise-producing machines. Construction jobs are notorious disturbers of the peace; perhaps the number-one culprit of all is the pneumatic pavement breaker. The list of bothersome noisemakers is almost endless. Assorted sirens, whistles, and bells sound at unexpected hours. Furnaces and air conditioners rumble and chug. Even crickets, pigeons, and starlings are capable of creating an intolerable racket.

There are three ways in which an engineer can approach these nuisances. First, he can seek to minimize the noise at the source. This sometimes poses a more difficult technological problem than the original invention of the noise-making mechanism itself. Second, he can separate the source of noise from the people who might be disturbed by it. This is a matter of foresight and sensible planning. Third, he can shield the individual from the noises about him.

Prevention, isolation, and insulation—these, then, are the approaches which the engineer can use in tackling the problem of audible disturbances. But the absence of *all* noise cannot be considered a desirable goal. On the contrary, psychological tests have shown that complete silence is literally maddening. No, clearly the engineer's goal should be threefold: the minimizing of unpleasant sound, the tolerance of normal sound, and the encouragement of pleasing sound.

The encouragement of pleasing sound

The last of these objectives confronts us with a bewildering problem. What are the standards by which we are to evaluate "pleasing sound?" Are we to set up loudspeakers in the streets and saturate the air with Beethoven sonatas? Surely not. Even beautiful music, if it is thrust forcefully upon a captive audience, can become distasteful.

To the extent that we are involved in community planning, engineers should seek first to provide adequate *facilities* for music, facilities such as concert halls and opera houses which enrich a community without intruding on individual privacy. When it comes to sound which is to be shared involuntarily by entire segments of the populace, then the planner must tread ever so carefully. The acceptable possibilities are limited, but they do exist.

Many a town hall has a clock which strikes the hours in a way that seems to grace the town with cohesiveness and tradition. Church bells proclaim the sanctity and joy of life. Band concerts bring festivity to a summer's evening. Parade music makes holidays gala. Harbor noises evoke the enchantment of the sea. Thundering surf, roaring waterfall, and rippling stream provide a never-ending source of pleasure to those people fortunate enough to live near them. Fountains are so delightfully soothing to the ear that it is surprising to consider how few there are in both public and private places. A crackling fire bespeaks welcome and good fellowship, a fact that is well-known to innkeepers, but virtually ignored by storekeepers and designers of public buildings. Song birds bring cheer and tidings of the changing seasons. The wind whispering in the trees carries a message of its own; and in some foreign lands the wind is gently harnessed so that it rustles bamboo curtains or tinkles strands of small bells.

Many sounds of the past have disappeared, making the world somewhat the poorer for their going. The "oyez" of the town crier, the "all's well" of the night watch, the "extra" of the newsboy, the call of the street vendor, the tune of the organ grinder—all served to give communities a reassuring sense of identity and an extra measure of humanity. A faint echo of these remains in the cheerful bells of the ice-cream truck calling to children in the summertime.

It can be said that there is not much that engineers can usefully do by way of stimulating pleasant sounds and that we are more than doing our share if we strive to eliminate the disagreeable ones. Certainly engineers do not have the last word in these matters, but what influence we do carry can well be used on the side of harmony and loveliness. A fountain integrated into the design of a traffic interchange or pedestrian plaza, a bandstand incorporated into a public square, a bird refuge salvaged from the encroachment of an industrial park, a bell tower surreptitiously included in an urban renewal plan—in his way the musically sensitive engineer can strike many a blow for the cause of beauty.

The tangible and the tenuous

Music and engineering, as we have seen, have many interests and goals in common. This does not alter the fact that there are striking differences between the art and the profession. Engineering deals with the tangible; music with the tenuous. Engineering aims toward the practical; music strives for the ineffable. Engineering's goals relate to daily living and the foreseeable future; music is conceived against a backdrop of eternity.

Engineering, like most of the arts, flourishes in time of peace and prosperity, when investment capital is available and confidence in the future runs high. With music there is much evidence that exactly the opposite is the case. Through years of stability and expanding wealth England produced little music of note, while in times of torment and violence Italy and Germany brought forth some of the most glorious music ever composed. Romain Rolland has explained the paradox in this way:

> One might even say that the plastic arts in general have need of luxury and leisure, of refined society, and of a certain equilibrium in civilization, in order to develop themselves fully. But when material conditions are harder, when life is bitter, starved, and harassed with care, when the opportunity of outside development is withheld, then the spirit is forced back upon itself, and its eternal need of happiness drives it to other outlets; its expression of beauty is changed and takes a less external character, and it seeks refuge in more intimate arts, such as poetry and music.[3]

Our own time surely has its share of luxury, leisure, and all of the other conditions conducive to engineering and art on a grand scale. Yet it is also a time of uncertainty and despair, of loneliness in the midst of multitudes, of barrenness in the midst of plenty. In short, it is an age which, in spite of all its apparent grandeur, desperately needs the refuge which music affords.

This refuge is of a completely different kind from anything

that we engineers can ever hope to construct. We would do well to seek solace and refreshment in it for ourselves and for our society.

Recommended reading

The number of books which deal with the relationship between music and engineering, or even music and science, is limited. However, there are several works that are very good. Outstanding is Arthur H. Benade, *Horns, Strings and Harmony* (Science Studies Series S11) which covers both the scientific and esthetic aspects of music. James Jeans, *Science and Music* (Cambridge University Press 143), although not the most recent treatment of the subject, is clear, informative, and engaging. Starting with the anatomical origin and workings of the human ear, Jeans carries the reader through the nature of sound, the principles of musical instruments, harmony and the musical scale, the effects of music on men and animals, and a review of acoustical theory.

Other meritorious works are Alexander Efron, *Sound* (John F. Rider 0093) and W. A. Van Bergeijk, John R. Pierce, and Edward E. David, Jr., *Waves and the Ear* (Science Studies Series S9).

Donald R. Griffin, *Echoes of Bats and Men* (Science Studies Series S4) is a most interesting book, recounting how sound waves are used by men and animals to provide information about the world around them.

A good, straightforward introduction to the basics of high fidelity is contained in Monroe Upton, *Electronics for Everyone* (Signet Science Library T2164).

For a comprehensive discussion of the physical and physiological aspects of sound, engineering methods of sound control, and personal protection from sound, refer to *Industrial Noise Manual* (American Industrial Hygiene Association, Detroit, Mich., 2nd Edition, 1966).

CHAPTER ELEVEN

The World
of Music

On a purely sensuous level anyone can enjoy music. And just about any listener can get a sense of the expressive meaning of a piece of music, whether it is cheerful or somber, tranquil or agitated. But the *purely musical meaning,* "in terms of the notes themselves and of their manipulation,"[1] is accessible only to those who have cultivated an understanding of musical language. Without some appreciation of music on the sheer musical plane, sound may pleasantly wash over us, but it can never quench our thirst or nourish our spirit.

Music has four essential elements: rhythm, melody, harmony, and tone-color or timbre. Utilizing these elements, the composer creates the structure of a musical work. His structure, to be coherent, must have recognizable form, and this form is usually achieved by some planned use of repetition. The three-part form is one that the student of music is early taught to recognize: an opening section, a contrasting middle part, and some kind of return to the beginning (A-B-A, in the usual terminology). The rondo is a form which features a principal theme returned to after each digression (A-B-A-C-A-D-A etc.). With a little attentive listening it is fairly easy to assimilate music constructed thus in logical sequence, "sectionally."

The composer is usually not content simply to string themes together sequentially. He may choose to modify a theme in a series of "variations." He may combine several themes in what is called "polyphonic" or "contrapuntal" design. He may utilize the classic "sonata" form, beginning with an "exposition" of contrasting themes, following with a "development" of these themes in different keys, and concluding with a "recapitulation." His structure may at times become quite complex. Our awareness of the musical form of his composition is the *sine qua non* of meaningful listening.

To understand music, then, we must be sensitive to its four elements; rhythm, melody, harmony, and tone-color, and conscious of the forms by which the composer shapes his work. Our "understanding"—let us be clear on this—can not take the shape of verbal expression. But this does not mean that music is necessarily vague and amorphous. Let us hear composer Roger Sessions on this difficult point:

> When, according to a well-known and possibly true anecdote, Beethoven in answer to a query as to the "meaning" of

his Eroíca Symphony turned to the piano and played the first bars of the work, he was, in effect, not only implying that its message could not be conveyed in any other way; he was also, and at least as clearly, implying that that message was something quite exact and precise, embodied in the tones, rhythms, harmonies, and dynamics of the passage.[2]

Tones and overtones

In addition to an awareness of the elements of music and its structure, it is helpful for us to remember something of its physical nature and its historical development.

Sound, we know, comes to our ear through the air in the form of vibrations. If a tone is sounded, its pitch is established by the frequency of the vibrations established in the air. The development of the art of music stems from the physical fact that when a tone is sounded, it creates *other* tones, higher and fainter, which sympathetically sound at the same time. These are called *overtones*. If we sound a C, the first overtone is half the wavelength, and twice the frequency, or C an octave higher. The second overtone is G, three times the frequency of the original C. The third overtone is another C, four times the frequency of the original C. The fourth overtone is E, five times the frequency, and so on, higher and fainter, until no longer audible. These overtones come out of, and are physically related to, the basic tone. They tend to "lead" toward the basic tone and they "sound right" in conjunction with it. Out of the first four different overtones (disregarding the repeated original tone) came the primitive five-note, or pentatonic, scale. Almost all the world's folk music is based on this scale, developed instinctively, stemming from basic physical relationships.

As civilization progressed, more overtones were added. In general a scale system can be defined as a chosen number of notes between a given tone and its octave. The given, or original, tone is called the "tonic" and it is the "home base" to which the other notes relate and to which they tend to lead. The tonic establishes the "key."

In our modern system we use a chromatic scale comprised of twelve roughly equal subdivisions of the octave, called semi-tones. The familiar do-re-mi-fa-sol-la-ti-do scale consists of seven notes out of the twelve, the second, fourth, seventh, ninth, and eleventh having been dropped to auxiliary status according to occidental taste and custom. This arrangement of seven notes is called the *diatonic scale in the major mode.*

Music through the Renaissance

About the music of the ancients we know very little. "What we truly know about their music could be written on the back of a visiting card, and what they say of it must remain either mysterious or incredible."[3]

What we know of medieval music comes to us mostly through the liturgical chants of the Roman Catholic Church. The scales or "modes" of the Middle Ages have a strange and somewhat Oriental sound to our ears.

During the Renaissance period the modern key feeling of the major and minor scales began to replace the old church modes. Polyphonic, or many-voiced, music, which had its origins in the Middle Ages, was developed to a high art. Originally composers of polyphonic music concentrated on "counterpoint," the delicate weaving together of two or more themes into a pleasing pattern. Out of the juxtaposition of different themes there evolved, accidentally but inevitably, a feeling for harmony. A harmonic style eventually developed which emphasized the topmost voice supported by chords, rather than several independent and equally important voices.

Although the musical instruments of the Renaissance were many and varied, the most impressive music of that period was vocal. Magnificent polyphonic settings of the Mass were composed. Polyphonic songs based on sacred texts were called motets. Similar to the motet, but written to a secular text in the vernacular, was the sprightly madrigal. Best-known composers of the period are the Netherlander, Orlando di Lasso (1532?–1594), William Byrd (1543–1623) of the Chapel Royal in London, and the illustrious Palestrina (1524?–1594) of the Papal Chapel in Rome.

Baroque music

Music written from the late 1500s to the middle 1700s is called, as are the examples of plastic art from this period, Baroque. The emotional force of the Catholic Counter Reformation inspired new and dramatic church music in Italy. From the north came the musical inspiration of the Protestant churches. And in every court all over Europe music was sought after and supported by the nobility.

Vocal music was still of great importance. The opera was born and became enormously popular (although the operas of this time were overshadowed by those of later periods and are rarely heard today). A form similar to opera, but set to a religious text and usually performed without scenery or costumes, was the oratorio. A choral work much like the oratorio but based upon the story of the New Testament was the Passion. Other popular vocal forms were the cantata, usually shorter than the oratorio; the chorale, a form of hymn incorporated into the church service by Martin Luther; and the ever-inspiring Mass.

Prominent instrumental forms were the fugue, a complex polyphonic design based upon a central subject, and short pieces in free style such as the prelude, the fantasia, and the toccata. Also popular were the suite, a succession of dances of contrasting rhythm; the sonata for solo instrument (not to be confused with the sonata *form* previously mentioned, nor with the later classic sonata); the concerto grosso, a composition in several movements in which two groups of instruments play in a form of "conversational" interchange; and the solo concerto, in which the "conversation" takes place between one instrument and a group.

Baroque music, which reached its culmination in the works of Handel (1685–1759) and the incomparable Johann Sebastian Bach (1685–1750), still contains a great deal of polyphony. The melodies are longer and more elaborate, less tuneful, than those of later periods. The music characteristically flows forward with great momentum.

In addition to Handel and Bach, great names of this period are the Italians Monteverdi (1567–1643), Frescobaldi (1583–1644), Corelli (1653–1713), Alessandro Scarlatti (1659–1725), Vivaldi (1680?–1743), and Domenico Scarlatti (1685–1757); the Frenchmen Lully (1633–1687), Couperin (1668–1733), and Rameau (1683–1764); the Englishman Purcell (1658–1695); and the German Buxtehude (1637–1707).

The classic era

We have had occasion to discuss the implications of the term "classical" in literature and in the fine arts. In music the "classic period" extends from the mid-eighteenth century into the Romantic revolution of the early nineteenth century. The eminent musician and teacher, Douglas Moore, defines the classic style in music as

> . . . characterized by fine sense of roundness of form, equilibrium of means of expression and content, discipline of mind, and an absence of any vulgar or sensational effects, especially the overemphasis of emotional content which made its appearance in a later age . . . .[4]

During this time the string quartet, the classic symphony, the classic sonata, and the concerto—primarily for piano or violin—came into their own. Opera, under the influence of Gluck

(1714–1787), started on the road toward the great music drama of the nineteenth century.

Three names completely dominate the classic period, three of the most exalted names in all the creative arts: Franz Joseph Haydn (1732–1809), Wolfgang Amadeus Mozart (1756–1791), and Ludwig van Beethoven (1770–1827). None of these three greats stayed within the prescribed bounds of a narrowly defined classicism. Haydn, and, even more, Mozart, overcame all limitations through sheer musical inventiveness. Beethoven, a titan among men, poured more overt emotion into his music than had any previous composer. He was, truly, a Romantic. But, musically, although he strained the classical forms to the utmost, he remained essentially faithful to them. It is his combination of passion and discipline that has led many to regard him as the world's greatest composer.

The music of Romanticism

After Beethoven the flood-gates were opened. Music was swept up in a tide of Romanticism which did not recede until the coming of the twentieth century. Some observers of the musical scene, considering the taste of the musical public, would say that it has not receded yet.

Romanticism in music can be characterized as the stressing of emotional expressiveness at the sacrifice of formal structure. Beautiful melodic line and rich harmonies are prized. Polyphony almost disappears. Development becomes less clear.

In the nineteenth century there were many forces which nourished the growth of Romantic music. Romantic poetry and painting had their effect, of course. Democratic fervor and national patriotism were at a peak. Improvements in instruments, particularly the brass, made possible dramatic orchestral effects. The main audience for music no longer consisted of small groups of aristocrats gathered at polite musicales. Huge audiences thronged into concert halls in every major European city, and these audiences craved spine-tingling, theatrical music. To these factors must be added the continual experimentation of the artist, who strives always for new effects, new and more daring harmonies.

Among the many great and familiar names of this period are: Weber (1786–1826), Schubert (1797–1828), Mendelssohn (1809–1847), Chopin (1809–1849), Schumann (1810–1856), Berlioz (1803–1869), Liszt (1811–1886), Wagner (1813–1883), Verdi (1813–1901), Franck (1822–1890), Bizet (1838–1875), Brahms (1833–1897), Bruckner (1824–1896), Tchaikovsky (1840–1893), Rimsky-Korsakov (1844–1908).

The Romantics brought lyric song, grand opera, and piano music to new heights. With the symphony and chamber music their success was less impressive. They bubbled over into new forms such as the symphonic poem, in which, although the music is not strictly representational, it pertains to a program or story.

The Romantic tradition was carried on into the twentieth century by such well-known composers as Gustav Mahler (1860–1911), Richard Strauss (1864–1949), and Sergei Rachmaninoff (1873–1943). But with orchestras growing ever larger, harmonies richer, and crescendos louder, a saturation point was bound to be reached.

The coming of modern music

In fact the search for new frontiers of sound had reached a crisis before the end of the nineteenth century in the music of a man whose works were the crowning glory of German Romanticism, Richard Wagner. Not only were Wagner's chords rich with overtones that sounded barbaric to ears attuned to more basic harmonies, but he actually stretched the entire concept of tonality to the breaking point. He changed key so frequently and with such abandon that the listener hardly knew what key he was in, or to what tonic note he would return.

As the twentieth century dawned, the French genius, Claude Debussey (1862–1918), continued the exploration of new harmonic possibilities. But he opposed a quiet sensousness against what he considered to be the bombastic overstatement of German Romanticism. Although he is considered to be one of the great and important composers, his style of "Impressionism," somewhat allied to the painting movement of the same name, had a short-lived vogue. Another French master, Maurice Ravel (1875–1937), toyed briefly with Impressionism, only to discard it in favor of a more precise and structured style.

A very different movement of the early twentieth century, identified with the name of Igor Stravinsky (1882–   ), was that of the "Primitives." They rebelled against the viscous, flowing quality of both Romanticism and Impressionism, and sought inspiration in the harsh rhythms of Russian folk songs and other primitive music. When Stravinsky's ballet, *The Rites of Spring*, was first performed in Paris in 1913, the musical world was stunned. Jagged and uncouth rhythms, meters changing in each bar—nothing like this had ever been heard before.

Tonality abandoned

In Germany, meanwhile, the Wagnerian legacy was giving rise to an even more startling development. Arnold Schoenberg (1874–1951) carried the concept of shifting tonalities to its logical conclusion by abandoning tonality altogether. Starting in 1906 he wrote "atonal" music in which there was no key. Each of the twelve notes of the chromatic scale had "equal rights." By 1913 he had developed "twelve-tone" music, in which a self-imposed rule compels the composer to sound each of the twelve tones of the chromatic scale before repeating a single tone.

Just as arguments about atonal music were rising in intensity, another new style appeared known as "polytonal." The composers of this school wrote melodies that are tonal, but melodies of different keys are played simultaneously. Leading exponents of polytonality were *Les Six,* six young French composers whose mentor was Erik Satie (1866–1925). Three of the six have become important figures in twentieth-century music: Arthur Honegger (1892–1955), Darius Milhaud (1892–   ) and Francis Poulenc (1899–1963).

In the 1920s yet another style came to the fore. Inspired by contrapuntal music of the past, the German composer, Paul Hindemith (1895–1963) wrote "neoclassic" pieces, atonal at first, then later reflecting a trend back toward tonality. Stravinsky, abandoning his Primitive rhythms, also proclaimed himself a neoclassicist.

Thus out of Wagnerian Romanticism there developed new and more experimental harmonies, leading to atonal music and the twelve-tone school. In rebellion against nineteenth-century music came daring new rhythms, polytonality, and a renewed respect for counterpoint and classic discipline.

Modern music and the public

Twentieth-century audiences have come to accept the new rhythms. Stravinsky hardly seems violent to us now. New harmonies, too, have become more and more palatable. What seemed unbearably dissonant in the 1920s has a pleasant tang to our ear today. Our "popular" music reflects our growing sophistication in harmonics and rhythm.

But atonal, twelve-tone, and polytonal music are still a long way from public acceptance. Hundreds of years of familiarity with melodies based on the diatonic scale cannot be obliterated in just a few decades.

Those modern composers who have won the most by way of public acceptance are those who have been bold in the realm of rhythm and harmony yet conservative in adhering to structure and tonality. Among the most popular: Sergei Prokofiev (1891–1953) and Dimitri Shostakovitch (1906–   ) of Russia; Bela Bartok (1881–1945) of Hungary; Jean Sibelius (1865–1957) of Finland; Ralph Vaughan Williams (1872–1958), William Walton (1902–   ), and Benjamin Britten (1913–   ) of England; Heitor Villa-Lobos (1887–1959) of Brazil; Aaron Copland (1900–   ), Virgil Thomson (1896–   ), and Samuel Barber (1910–   ) of the United States.

Music of the future

The ways in which serious music will develop in the years ahead are uncertain. New frontiers are constantly being explored.

Milton Babbitt has taken Schoenberg's twelve-tone system and applied its strict serial rules not only to pitch, but to duration, register, dynamics, and timbre as well. Many of his complex pieces are composed on tape by means of the Mark II Electronic Music Synthesizer, a fantastic conglomeration of sound-generating devices such as tuning forks, oscillators, and frequency multipliers.

John Cage has moved in a totally different direction, creating "indeterminate" or "unintentional" compositions based on "chance" patterns. These patterns are derived from tossed coins or some equally nonpersonal source. Other Cage compositions feature radios, tape recorders, and phonographs playing haphazardly together.

As with philosophy and the fine arts, we engineers find ourselves attracted to the technological bias of much contemporary music, but repelled by its lack of humanistic content. If "Cage's music is essentially an exploration of indeterminacy," and "Babbitt's subject is literally the permutations of serial patterns,"[5] then this new music obviously has an appeal to the mathematically educated listener. Yet it too often seems to chill rather than warm, depress rather than inspire.

Fortunately in music, as in all the arts, we are not confronted with a choice of "either/or." Music of all types and periods will reward our listening. Experimental and traditional, classic and romantic, contrapuntal and harmonic, atonal and tonal—each style has its valid message, each reflects one of the myriad faces of beauty and truth.

"To listen intently . . ."

Having said these few words about music, let us close by stating the self-evident truth that talk about music is empty in comparison with the experience of listening to music. Let us listen, and listen well.

"To listen intently," says Aaron Copland, "to listen consciously, to listen with one's whole intelligence is the least we can do in the furtherance of an art that is one of the glories of mankind."[6]

With this ringing exhortation it seems appropriate to bring to an end our brief review of the liberal arts. "To listen intently" is the least we can do in the furtherance of all of the arts, not only music. Let the final word come from physicist J. Robert Oppenheimer, a member of that small but growing group of men who have shown us that a successful professional career need not preclude a profound interest in the humanities:

> I think we have, all of us, to preserve our competence in our own professions, to preserve what we know intimately, to preserve our mastery. This is, in fact, our only anchor in honesty. We need also to be open to other and complementary lives, not intimidated by them and not contemptuous of them . . . . As a start, we must learn again, without contempt and with great patience, to talk to one another; and we must hear.[7]

Recommended reading

The definitive historical work is Paul Henry Lang, *Music in Western Civilization* (W. W. Norton, 1941). Briefer and useful: Douglas Moore, *A Guide to Musical Styles, From Madrigal to Modern Music* (W. W. Norton N200), and Alfred Einstein, *A Short History of Music* (Vintage Books V4).

A good introduction to the technical side of music is Aaron Copland, *What to Listen for in Music* (Mentor Books MP546).

An overflowing grab bag of fiction, articles, biography, and letters dealing with music is Jacques Barzun (ed.), *Pleasures of Music* (Compass Books C68).

Recommended listening

Wherever possible music should be heard "live" in the concert hall. There is an immediacy, an excitement, about a live performance that can not be duplicated by even the finest recording.

Of course, in this age of high fidelity, listening to records at home runs concert going an increasingly close second.

For those interested in the systematic approach to "music appreciation," *The Story of Great Music* is recommended. Produced by Time-Life Records, Time & Life Building, Chicago, Illinois 60611, these packages of recordings, educational text, and art reproductions are attractive and comprehensive.

For the listener who prefers to build his collection in accordance with his own taste, the following list of 100 "basic" recordings should prove useful. It was prepared by Martin Bookspan, Music Director of radio station WQXR, New York. Since new recordings of these works are being issued constantly, no recommended performances are listed.

BACH, JOHANN SEBASTIAN

> *Brandenburg Concertos*
> *Mass in B Minor*
> *Passion According to Saint Matthew*

BARTOK, BELA

> *Concerto for Orchestra*

BEETHOVEN, LUDWIG VAN

Piano Concerto #4 in G
Piano Concerto #5 in E Flat, "Emperor"
Violin Concerto in D
Missa Solemnis in D
Symphony #3 in E Flat
Symphony #5 in C Minor
Symphony #6 in F, "Pastoral"
Symphony #7 in A
Symphony #9 in D Minor
"Moonlight" and "Pathetique" Piano Sonatas
(Sonatas Nos. 14 in C Sharp Minor and 8 in C Minor)
String Quartet No. 14 in C Sharp Minor
Trio No. 7 in B Flat, "Archduke"
Violin & Piano Sonata #9 in A, "Kreutzer"

BERLIOZ, HECTOR

Romeo and Juliet
Symphonie Fantastique

BIZET, GEORGES

Carmen

BRITTEN, BENJAMIN

War Requiem

BRAHMS, JOHANNES

Piano Concerto #1 in D Minor
Piano Concerto #2 in B Flat
Violin Concerto in D
Double Concerto in A Minor
Piano Quartet #1 in G Minor
Symphony #1 in C Minor
Symphony #4 in E Minor
A German Requiem

BRUCKNER, ANTON

Symphony #9 in D Minor

CHOPIN, FREDERIC

Piano Sonatas Nos. 2 in B Flat Minor and *3 in B Minor*
Fourteen Waltzes

COPLAND, AARON

Appalachian Spring

DEBUSSY, CLAUDE

La Mer
Preludes for Piano

DVORAK, ANTONIN

Cello Concerto in B Minor
*Symphony #8 in G**
*Symphony #9 in E Minor, "From the New World"***
**sometimes erroneously listed as #4*
***sometimes erroneously listed as #5*

GERSHWIN, GEORGE

Rhapsody in Blue and *An American in Paris*

FRANCK, CÉSAR

Symphony in D Minor

GRIEG, EDVARD

Piano Concerto in A Minor

HANDEL, GEORGE FREDERICK

Messiah
The Water Music

HAYDN, FRANZ JOSEF

Symphony #94 in G, "Surprise"
Missa Solemnis in D Minor, "Lord Nelson Mass"

LISZT, FRANZ

Piano Concertos Nos. 1 in E Flat and *2 in A*
Piano Music

MAHLER, GUSTAV

Das Lied von der Erde
Symphony #1 in D, "Titan"

MENDELSSOHN, FELIX

Symphony #3 in A Minor, "Scottish"
Symphony #4 in A, "Italian"
Violin Concerto in E Minor
A Midsummer Night's Dream

MOUSSORGSKY, MODESTE

Boris Godounov
Pictures at an Exhibition (Ravel Orchestration)

MOZART, WOLFGANG AMADEUS

Clarinet Quintet in A
Don Giovanni
The Marriage of Figaro
Piano Concerto #20 in D Minor
Symphony #40 in G Minor
Symphony #41 in C, "Jupiter"

PAGANINI, NICOLO

Violin Concerto #1 in D

PROKOFIEFF, SERGE

Peter and the Wolf
Symphony #5 in B Flat

PUCCINI, GIACOMO

La Boheme
Madame Butterfly
Tosca

RACHMANINOFF, SERGEI

Piano Concerto #2 in C Minor

RAVEL, MAURICE

Daphnis and Chloe
L'Enfant et les Sortileges

RIMSKY-KORSAKOFF, NICOLAI

Scheherazade

SAINT SAENS, CAMILLE

Symphony #3 in C Minor, "Organ"

SCHUBERT, FRANZ

Quintet in A for Piano and Strings, "Trout"
Quintet in C for Strings
Symphony #8 in B Minor, "Unfinished"
Symphony #9 in C, "Great"

SCHUMANN, ROBERT

Piano Concerto in A Minor
Piano Quintet in E Flat
Symphony #4 in D Minor

SHOSTAKOVITCH, DMITRI

Symphony #5

SIBELIUS, JEAN

Symphony #2 in D
Symphony #5 in E Flat

STRAUSS, RICHARD

Don Juan and *Till Eulenspiegel's Merry Pranks*
Don Quixote
Der Rosenkavalier

STRAVINSKY, IGOR

Petrouchka
Le Sacre du Printemps

TCHAIKOVSKY, PETER ILYITCH

Piano Concerto #1 in B Flat Minor
Violin Concerto in D
The Sleeping Beauty
Symphony #4 in F Minor
Symphony #5 in E Minor
Symphony #6 in B Minor, "Pathétique"

VERDI, GIUSEPPE

Aida
Requiem
Rigoletto
La Traviata

VIVALDI, ANTONIO

The Four Seasons

WAGNER, RICHARD

Die Meistersinger
Die Walkure

Notes

Chapter 1

1. Earl J. McGrath, *Liberal Education in the Professions,* Teachers College, Columbia University, New York, 1959, p. 20.
2. Lewis Mumford, "From Erewhon to Nowhere," in Thomas Parke Hughes (ed.), *The Development of Western Technology Since 1500,* The Macmillan Company, New York, 1964, p. 22.
3. New England Consultants, Inc., *The Engineer Today,* prepared for Esso Research and Engineering Company, 1963, p. 10.
4. J. J. Dougherty, "The Engineer Among People," *American Engineer,* July, 1966.
5. Gilbert W. Chapman, "Specific Needs for Leadership in Management," in Robert A. Goldwin and Charles A. Nelson (eds.), *Toward the Liberally Educated Executive,* Mentor Books, New American Library of World Literature, Inc., New York, 1960, p. 10.
6. Marcus Vitruvius Pollio, "Selections from De Architectura," in Walter J. Miller and Leo E. A. Saidla (eds.), *Engineers as Writers,* D. Van Nostrand Co., Inc., Princeton, N.J., 1953, p. 14.
7. Mark Van Doren, *Liberal Education,* Beacon Press, Boston, 1959, p. 16.
8. Quoted in Benjamin Farrington, *Greek Science,* Penguin Books, Inc., Baltimore, 1944, pp. 28–29.
9. Ralph Waldo Emerson, "Works and Days," in Arthur O. Lewis, Jr.

(ed.), *Of Men and Machines*, E. P. Dutton & Co., Inc., New York, 1963, p. 69.

10. Thomas H. Huxley, "Science and Culture," in John J. Cadden and Patrick R. Brostowin (eds.), *Science and Literature*, D. C. Heath and Co., Boston, 1964, p. 11.

11. Thorstein Veblen, *The Engineers and the Price System*, Harcourt, Brace & World, Inc., New York, 1963, pp. 139–140. Originally appeared as a series of essays in *The Dial* in 1919.

12. Earl Ubell, quoted in "Public Relations Seminar for the Engineering Profession," *American Engineer*, March, 1966.

13. Arthur Garratt (ed.), *Penguin Technology Survey 1966*, Penguin Books, Inc., Baltimore, 1966, p. 8.

14. William Ruder, "A Public Relations Executive Looks at the Engineer and His Role in Today's Society," *American Engineer*, March, 1966.

15. New England Consultants, Inc., *The Engineer Today*, prepared for Esso Research and Engineering Company, 1963, p. 35.

16. Richard D. Blanchard, quoted in "Public Relations Seminar for the Engineering Profession," *American Engineer*, March, 1966.

17. James Reston, *The New York Times*, December 13, 1964.

18. R. Buckminster Fuller, "Vision 65 Summary Lecture," *The American Scholar*, Spring, 1966.

19. George Orwell, "The Road to Wigan Pier," in Arthur O. Lewis, Jr. (ed.), *Of Men and Machines*, E. P. Dutton & Co., Inc., New York, 1963, p. 259.

20. Jacques Ellul, *The Technological Society*, trans. John Wilkinson, Alfred A. Knopf, Inc., New York, 1964. Passage was reprinted in *The Saturday Review*, February 6, 1965.

21. Quoted in Don K. Price, *The Scientific Estate*, Harvard University Press, Cambridge, 1965, p. 57.

22. See Don K. Price, *The Scientific Estate*, Harvard University Press, Cambridge, 1965, and Jay M. Gould, *The Technical Elite*, Augustus M. Kelley, New York, 1966.

23. Lewis Mumford, "From Erewhon to Nowhere," in Thomas Park Hughes (ed.), *The Development of Western Technology Since 1500*, The Macmillan Company, New York, 1964, p. 26.

24. Lynn White, Jr., "Humanism and the Education of Engineers," *Studies of Courses and Sequences in Humanities, Fine Arts and Social Sciences for Engineering Students*, University of California, Department of Engineering, Los Angeles, 1963, p. 53.

25. Eric Ashby, *Technology and the Academics*, Macmillan & Co. Ltd., London, 1963, p. 81.

26. Jacques Barzun, *Classic, Romantic and Modern*, Anchor Books, Doubleday & Co., Inc., Garden City, N.Y., 1961, p. 148. Copyright 1943, © 1961 by Jacques Barzun, with permission of Atlantic Monthly Press, Little, Brown and Company, Boston.

27. Eric Ashby, *Technology and the Academics*, Macmillan & Co. Ltd., London, 1963, p. 84.

Chapter 2

1. Samuel Smiles, "The Engineers and the Industrial Revolution," in Thomas Parke Hughes (ed.), *The Development of Western Technology Since 1500*, The Macmillan Company, New York, 1964, p. 85.
2. James Kip Finch, *The Story of Engineering*, Anchor Books, Doubleday & Company, Inc., Garden City, N.Y., 1960, p. xxvii.
3. Hans Straub, *A History of Civil Engineering*, trans. E. Rockwell, Leonard Hill Ltd., London, 1952, p. 1.
4. L. Sprague de Camp, *The Ancient Engineers*, Doubleday & Co., Inc., Garden City, N.Y., 1963, p. 13.
5. Richard Kostelanetz, "Understanding McLuhan (In Part)," *The New York Times Magazine*, January 29, 1967.
6. Richard S. Kirby, Sidney Withington, Arthur B. Darling, and Frederick G. Kilgour, *Engineering in History*, McGraw-Hill Book Company, New York, 1956, p. 504.
7. Quoted in Hans Straub, *A History of Civil Engineering*, trans. E. Rockwell, Leonard Hill Ltd., London, 1952, p. 117.
8. Lynn White, Jr., "On Intellectual Gloom," *The American Scholar*, Spring, 1966.
9. A comprehensive list of inventions and their dates is included in Lewis Mumford, *Technics and Civilization*, Harcourt, Brace & World, Inc., New York, 1934; reissued by Harbinger Books. Tables showing time-relations of selected events in technological history, both to each other and to named events in general history, are to be found at the end of T. K. Derry and Trevor I. Williams, *A Short History of Technology*, Oxford University Press, London, 1961. A useful chronological table listing important scientific and engineering works, as well as birth and death dates of great scientists and engineers, is included in Hans Straub, *A History of Civil Engineering*, trans. E. Rockwell, Leonard Hill Ltd., London, 1952.
10. T. K. Derry and Trevor I. Williams, *A Short History of Technology*, Oxford University Press, Oxford, 1961, p. 193.
11. Lynn White, Jr., *Medieval Technology and Social Change*, Oxford University Press, Oxford, 1962, p. 38.
12. Lewis Mumford, *Technics and Civilization*, Harcourt, Brace & World, Inc., New York, 1934; reissued by Harbinger Books, p. 118.
13. *Ibid.*, p. 14.

Chapter 3

1. Voltaire, "The New Philosophical History," in Fritz Stern (ed.), *The Varieties of History*, The World Publishing Company, Cleveland, 1956, p. 36.
2. *Ibid.*, p. 44.
3. George M. Trevelyan, "Clio Rediscovered," in Fritz Stern (ed.), *The*

Varieties of History, The World Publishing Company, Cleveland, 1956, p. 236.

4. Jacques Barzun, "Cultural History as a Synthesis," in Fritz Stern (ed.), *The Varieties of History,* The World Publishing Company, Cleveland, 1956, p. 398.

5. Edith Hamilton, *The Roman Way,* Mentor Books, New American Library of World Literature, Inc., New York, 1957, p. 115. Copyright 1932 by W. W. Norton & Company, Inc., New York. Copyright renewed 1960 by Edith Hamilton. Reprinted by permission from W. W. Norton & Company, Inc.

6. *Ibid.,* pp. 151–152.

7. Crane Brinton (ed.), *The Portable Age of Reason Reader,* The Viking Press, Inc., New York, 1956, p. 17.

8. Charles Frankel, *The Case for Modern Man,* Beacon Press, Boston, 1959, p. 206.

9. Basil Willey, "How the Scientific Revolution of the Seventeenth Century Affected Other Branches of Thought," in *A Short History of Science,* Anchor Books, Doubleday & Company, Inc., Garden City, N.Y., 1959, p. 68.

Chapter 4

1. Robert Louis Stevenson, *Across the Plains,* Charles Scribner's Sons, New York, 1898, pp. 49–50.

2. George Madison Priest (trans., ed.), Goethe's *Faust,* Alfred A. Knopf, Inc., New York, 1941, p. 418.

3. John W. Campbell, Jr., "The Place of Science Fiction," *Modern Science Fiction, Its Meaning and Its Future,* Coward-McCann, Inc., New York, 1953, p. 17.

4. Robert A. Heinlein, *The Science Fiction Novel,* Advent Publishers, Chicago, 1959, p. 47.

5. Aldous Huxley, *Literature and Science,* Harper & Row, Publishers, Inc., New York, 1963, p. 44.

Chapter 5

1. M. I. Finley (ed.), *The Portable Greek Historians,* The Viking Press, Inc., New York, 1959, p. 13.

2. Moses Hadas, *A History of Greek Literature,* Columbia University Press, New York, 1950, p. 75.

3. John Ciardi, "An Ulcer, Gentlemen, Is an Unwritten Poem," in Robert A. Goldwin and Charles A. Nelson (eds.), *Toward the Liberally Educated Executive,* Mentor Books, New American Library of World Literature, Inc., New York, 1960, p. 67.

4. Quoted in Stephen Spender, "The Connecting Imagination," in Richard

Thruelsen and John Kobler (eds.), *Adventures of the Mind*, Alfred A. Knopf, Inc., New York, 1961, p. 30.

5. John Ciardi, "An Ulcer, Gentlemen, Is an Unwritten Poem," in Robert A. Goldwin and Charles A. Nelson, eds., *Toward the Liberally Educated Executive*, Mentor Books, New American Library of World Literature, New York, 1960, p. 69.

6. Elizabeth Drew, *The Novel, A Modern Guide to Fifteen English Masterpieces*, Dell Publishing Co., Inc., New York, 1963, pp. 20–21.

7. Lionel Trilling, *The Liberal Imagination*, Anchor Books, Doubleday & Company, Inc., New York, N.Y., 1953, pp. 214–215; reissued Viking Press, Inc., New York, 1950.

8. *Ibid.*, p. 206.

9. Lionel Trilling, *Beyond Culture*, The Viking Press, Inc., New York, 1965, p. 30.

Chapter 6

1. Norwood Russell Hanson, *Patterns of Discovery*, Cambridge University Press, London, 1958, p. 126.

2. Erwin Schrödinger, *Science Theory and Man*, Dover Publications, Inc., New York, 1957, p. 212.

3. Sir James Jeans, *Physics and Philosophy*, Ann Arbor Paperbacks, University of Michigan Press, Ann Arbor, Mich., 1958, p. 203.

4. William S. Beck, *Modern Science and the Nature of Life*, Harcourt, Brace, & World, Inc., New York, 1957, pp. 242–243.

5. J. A. V. Butler, *Inside the Living Cell*, George Allen and Unwin Ltd., London, 1959, p. 156.

6. William S. Beck, *Modern Science and the Nature of Life*, Harcourt, Brace and Co., New York, 1957, p. 140.

7. Sir James Jeans, *Physics and Philosophy*, Ann Arbor Paperbacks, University of Michigan Press, Ann Arbor, Mich., 1958, p. 216.

8. L. Susan Stebbing, *Philosophy and the Physicists*, Dover Publications, Inc., New York, 1958, p. 213.

9. Quoted in *ibid.*, p. 186.

10. Quoted in *ibid.*, p. 186.

11. Philipp Frank, *Philosophy of Science*, Prentice-Hall, Inc., Englewood Cliffs, N.J., 1957, p. 255.

12. Erwin Schrödinger, *What Is Life?*, Anchor Books, Doubleday and Company, Inc., Garden City, N.Y., 1956, p. 105.

13. Sir Charles Sherrington, *Man on His Nature*, Cambridge University Press, London, 1953, p. 229.

14. Bertrand Russell, *My Philosophical Development*, Simon and Schuster, Inc., New York, 1959, p. 64.

15. J. Bronowski, *Science and Human Values*, Harper Torchbooks, Harper & Row, Publishers, New York, 1959, p. 80.

16. Bertrand Russell, *Mysticism and Logic*, Anchor Books, Doubleday & Company, Inc., Garden City, N.Y., 1957, p. 29.

17. Quoted in Charles Coulston Gillispie, *The Edge of Objectivity*, Princeton University Press, Princeton, N.J., 1960, p. 520.
18. William James, *Pragmatism*, Meridian Books, Inc., New York, 1955, p. 42.
19. Martin Buber, *Eclipse of God*, Harper Torchbooks, Harper & Row, Publishers, New York, 1957, p. 5.
20. Karl Jaspers, *Reason and Existenz*, Noonday Books, Farrar, Straus & ·Cudahy, Inc., New York, 1957, p. 126.
21. Walter Kaufmann (ed.), *Existentialism from Dostoevsky to Sartre*, Meridian Books, Inc., New York, 1956, p. 51.

Chapter 7

1. William James, *Pragmatism*, Meridian Books, Inc., New York, 1955, p. 18.
2. Bertrand Russell, *My Philosophical Development*, Simon and Schuster, Inc., New York, 1959, p. 250.
3. Anne Fremantle, *The Age of Belief*, Houghton Mifflin Company, Boston, 1957, pp. 14–15.
4. Bertrand Russell, *My Philosophical Development*, Simon and Schuster, Inc., New York, 1959, p. 254.

Chapter 8

1. Walter Gropius, "The Curse of Conformity," in Richard Thruelsen and John Kobler (eds.), *Adventures of the Mind*, Alfred A. Knopf, Inc., New York, 1959, p. 263.
2. Lewis Mumford, *Art and Technics*, Columbia University Press, New York, 1952, pp. 63–64.
3. Bernard Berenson, *Rumor & Reflection*, Simon and Schuster, Inc., New York, 1952, p. 216.
4. Lewis Mumford, *Art and Technics*, Columbia University Press, New York, 1952, pp. 80–82.
5. John Dewey, *The Quest for Certainty*, Capricorn Books, G. P. Putnam's Sons, New York, 1960, p. 262; copyright 1929 by John Dewey.

Chapter 9

1. Herbert Read, *The Meaning of Art*, Faber & Faber, Ltd., London, 1931, p. 197; reissued Penguin Books, Inc., Baltimore, 1949.
2. *Ibid.*, p. 129.
3. H. W. Janson and Dora Jane Janson, *The Picture History of Painting*, Washington Square Press, Inc., New York, 1961, p. 166.
4. *Ibid.*, p. 191.

5. H. W. Janson, *History of Art,* Harry N. Abrams, Inc., New York, 1962, p. 533.
6. Allan Kaprow, "The Legacy of Jackson Pollock," *Art News,* October, 1958.
7. Alan Solomon, "The New Art," catalog of "The Popular Image" exhibition, Washington Gallery of Modern Art, 1963.
8. Susan Sontag, "Non-Writing and the Art Scene," *Book Week, The New York Herald-Tribune,* July 25, 1965.
9. John Rublowsky, quoted in Susan Sontag, "Nonwriting and the Art Scene," *Book Week, The New York Herald-Tribune,* July 25, 1965.
10. Leo Steinberg, "Contemporary Art and the Plight of Its Public," in Gregory Battcock (ed.), *The New Art,* E. P. Dutton & Co., Inc., New York, 1966, p. 44.
11. Lawrence Alloway, "Notes on Op Art," in Gregory Battcock (ed.), *The New Art,* Dutton Paperbacks, E. P. Dutton & Co., Inc., New York, 1966.
12. *Ibid.*
13. *Ibid.*
14. Alan Solomon, "The New Art," catalog of "The Popular Image" exhibition, Washington Gallery of Modern Art, 1963.

Chapter 10

1. Lewis Mumford, *Art and Technics,* Columbia University Press, New York, 1952, p. 8.
2. Paul Hindemith, *A Composer's World,* Anchor Books, Doubleday & Company, Inc., Garden City, N.Y., 1961, p. 9.
3. David Ewen (ed.) *Romain Rolland's Essays on Music,* Dover Publications, Inc., New York, 1959, p. 9.

Chapter 11

1. Aaron Copland, *What to Listen for in Music,* Mentor Books, New American Library of World Literature, Inc., New York, p. 21.
2. Roger Sessions, *The Musical Experience of Composer, Performer, Listener,* Princeton University Press, Princeton, N.J., 1958, p. 25.
3. Jacques Barzun (ed.), *Pleasures of Music,* Compass Books, The Viking Press, Inc., New York, 1960, p. 5.
4. Douglas Moore, *From Madrigal to Modern Music,* W. W. Norton & Co., Inc., New York, 1942, pp. 97–98.
5. Richard Kostelanetz, "Milton Babbitt and John Cage are the Two Extremes of Avant-Garde Music," *The New York Times Magazine,* January 15, 1967.
6. Aaron Copland, *What to Listen for in Music,* Mentor Books, New American Library of World Literature, Inc. New York, p. 163.
7. J. Robert Oppenheimer, "Science & Culture," *Encounter,* October, 1962.

Index of Names and Titles

(not including names and titles in
"Recommended Reading" sections)

Subject Index